Published by FlatBear Publishing
PO Box 3679, Bath, UK. BA2 4WS

ISBN 978-1-910291-33-7

THANK YOU!

Thank you to all the wonderful knitters who have taken the time to send me your story and take part in our study. Please keep your wonderful yarns rolling in.

To all those members of Stitchlinks who have supported me along the way from around the world.

To my family, friends and colleagues who have helped with their professional knowledge, skills input, various resources and numerous cups of coffee.

Thank you for making my dream of writing this book a reality.

FOREWORD

Betsan kindly offered to send me a pre-print of her book, a book I had perhaps ungenerously referred to, when it was in the planning stage, as the 'Knitwits' Bible'. Her offer was not out of the blue – she and I first met some time ago and I have very much appreciated the conversations we have had, about pain, the brain, recovery and, of course, knitting, over the years.

There is no doubt that Betsan is a Knitting Crusader of the highest order (are there levels of Knitting Crusader? 'Pearl 1' has a nice ring to it and would look good on a credit card), but it is her journey to Crusader that got me interested. She has not, it seems, turned her passion into a treatment, nor has she made the very common mistake of presuming that *what appeared to work for me will work for everyone*'. Instead, she has made a discovery – that of other people's reflections of knitting – and integrated it with her training, her astute eye, her clinical reasoning, her open mind and, last but not least, her personal experience. She has then interrogated her new theory and enlisted the support of experts – scientists, knitters and patients – to satisfy herself that this is not a flash in the pan, but that it is a discovery with real promise.

Here, she has squeezed her formidable experience and startling journey into a book.

On reading it, you will be reminded of the unexampled magnificence of your brain and the splendid simplicity of knitting it to good health.

A simple yet powerful solution

On one level it is seductively simple – there is no doubt that without a brain, one could neither knit, nor hurt and it really does seem that doing the former reduces the latter.

Betsan's book is about so much more than knitting and pain. It is about embracing the complexity of how and why our brain produces experiences. It is about making things, giving things, sharing things, while you make your own journey to recovery. I suspect you will have a rewarding trip.

Lorimer Moseley, Professor of Clinical Neurosciences and Chair of Physiotherapy at The University of South Australia.

As assignments go, being sent to the Royal United Hospital in Bath, UK to record a radio programme about Therapeutic Knitting with a group of chronic pain patients for the charity Pain Concern would challenge the most creative of minds. Too depressing an environment, and too visual for radio. **How wrong could this producer be!**

Under Betsan's guidance, the Stitchlinks group of patients with serious lifelong pain conditions who could have sunk in the misery and isolation brought about by chronic pain, contradicted all expectations. Needles clickety-clacking away, relentless banter and laughter, pain banished – at least for now.

Paul Harvard-Evans, multi-award-winning radio producer. Producer of Airing Pain for the charity Pain Concern

This book is about your wellbeing and how you can use knitting as an extraordinary, flexible tool to enable you to live life well. The following chapters contain something for everyone, whether you are fit and well or living with a medical condition.

The intriguing fact about self-help books is that people keep buying them. The reality is that it is difficult to make lifestyle changes and change the way you think simply by reading a book. Making changes on your own, with just a book to support you, is difficult, it can drain your reserves and deplete your willpower, making you much more likely to succumb to other temptations.

It's difficult to stay strong 24/7 without support and a means of refuelling your energy and determination.

This book is different because it gives you a tool – THERAPEUTIC KNITTING – which will enable you to persevere, take control and manage the process of change.

The first half of the book explains how and why it works, the second half gets down to the 'doing' of Therapeutic Knitting.

Becoming engaged in 'doing' at the same time as enhancing your knowledge will help you translate your desire to change into action. The actual change you experience, by engaging in Therapeutic Knitting, has the power to transform your life. Therapeutic Knitting gives immediate, multisensory feedback which will stimulate positive thoughts, behaviours and emotional responses which you can use to enhance your wellbeing.

A simple yet powerful solution

Successful change needs perseverance and the ongoing 'small rewards' you will receive as you knit will help you to stay strong and fuel your reserves and willpower along your way to wellness.

This book integrates my medical knowledge and experience of many years as a clinician with recent research and data taken from the Stitchlinks / Cardiff University study[1] plus stories sent to me from knitters around the world. I have been using Therapeutic Knitting in my clinical practice since 2006.

The overwhelming messages in the numerous narratives received, and in the study which surveyed 3,514 knitters from 31 countries, were the same regardless of the different cultural, educational and health backgrounds knitters came from. Quotes throughout the book are taken with permission from the large number of knitters who have sent me their stories and contributed to our study. I haven't attributed these quotes to individuals in order to protect their identity as promised.

The information collected, combined with my medical knowledge, has informed my development of Therapeutic Knitting.

Therapeutic Knitting will provide you with an accessible tool to improve your wellbeing whether you are fit and well or living with a long-term medical condition.

Stitchlinks (**www.stitchlinks.com**) was created to support you on this journey. It provides free access to information, regular research updates and a forum of friends who understand and care.

The knowledge gathered in this book, used alongside knitting as a tool, will guide you on your way to wellness and show you how to knit a flexible mind, keep your reserves fuelled and your willpower strong.

The combination will help you succeed and keep you motivated.

A simple yet powerful solution

"Knitting requires me to think creatively, to plan, prepare, organise, co-ordinate and control just one small aspect of my life. Then any other changes are manageable."

"I found that knitting helped calm my thoughts, and while I was knitting and putting stitches in order it was easier to put my own mind in order."

"I liken knitting very much to meditation, my mind is empty while I knit, my breathing quiet, and everything apart from my hands very still..."

"Antidepressants numb all my senses. Knitting makes me happy!"

Real strength comes from flexibility not rigidity.

Knitting creates strong, resilient, flexible fabric.

Therapeutic Knitting seeks to create strong,
resilient, flexible minds in the process.

© Stitchlinks

A simple yet powerful solution

CONTENTS

CONTENTS

PROLOGUE

Join me in a journey of discovery

• •

The brilliant thing about knitting is...
it can literally change your mind
and provide a simple yet
powerful way to wellness...

Notes

This book is about how you can use the remarkable facts I have uncovered in my exploration of the therapeutic benefits of knitting. How it is possible to literally 'change your mind' to begin the process of healing and dealing with life with a smile whatever your starting point on that journey.

It's about your wellbeing and how you can use Therapeutic Knitting as an extraordinary tool to help you improve it.

I gave up my career as a senior physiotherapist in 2002 having become disillusioned with the system I found myself working in. Little did I know that this would be the beginning of an exciting journey which would lead me to investigate the world of neuroscience, pain, mental illness, wellbeing and knitting, taking me back into health care in a very different, but exciting role.

I have always been intrigued by how thoughts, beliefs and behaviour are so closely entwined with feelings. Thoughts, beliefs, behaviours and emotions can affect or cause illness as well as how you manage and heal. They can influence how you learn to cope and live a fulfilling life despite the enforced challenges life will inevitably throw your way. The way you think is closely entwined with the way you feel.

The key lies in the realisation that thoughts are not tangible events, they are concepts constructed by YOUR mind, and consequently YOU have the power to change them. Changing the way you think isn't easy but it is entirely possible.

A simple yet powerful solution

Knitting is a simple yet powerful tool that can help you begin that journey now and stay motivated and involved along the way. It will enable you to win, and help others win too.

This work weaves together my professional and personal experiences over a number of years.

I trained as a physiotherapist in a leading London teaching hospital which had a formidable reputation for high standards. The Middlesex Hospital was a grand Victorian institution situated just behind Oxford Street in Central London. It was a daunting but exciting place to be in the 1970s.

Many of the standards and working practices considered as important at the time have fallen by the wayside in modern healthcare systems. As a student, most of my training was 'hands on'. We learned to 'feel' problem areas through our hands. Touch played a pivotal part in our relationship with our patients.

All physiotherapy and medical students were obliged to spend a month working as nursing assistants. We worked shifts and were taught the basics of 'caring', which included washing and feeding vulnerable people. It was an invaluable experience. Importantly, it nurtured a knowledge of the patience and commitment involved in 'caring' and gave me huge admiration for the work carers and nurses perform on a daily basis.

Notes

Notes

After qualifying I continued to work for a year at the same hospital gaining experience in a range of clinical specialties. It was with this rather starched background that I applied for a job in a medical rehabilitation spa in Switzerland. I have to confess this was more about my love of skiing than for any clinical consideration, but the experience has proven to be invaluable in many ways.

It opened my eyes to whole-person care, which I believe is essential for long-term wellbeing and success in health care.

Health care in a Swiss medical rehabilitation spa was a bit of a shock to my system. The approach was in stark contrast to my strict, physiologically-focused training – as a physio I had been trained to treat knees and backs. The Swiss approach, however, treated the whole person who happened to have a problematic knee or back. It was real care which recognised the importance of the mind as pivotal to healing – as the wellspring of healing.

At first I was deeply suspicious of this approach and the strange sounding additional treatments my patients were prescribed – they weren't scientific enough for me. Patients were also prescribed individual and group hydrotherapy and exercise sessions. Individual sessions were aimed at identifying the specific exercises suitable for their particular problems, whereas the group sessions enabled them to enjoy moving and interacting in a social environment whilst

A simple yet powerful solution

focusing on general fitness. Dietary advice, various massage techniques and even sessions with the beauty therapist and hairdresser were prescribed by the doctors!

My rather rigid approach to physiological, joint and muscle problems gradually changed as I observed people improving and learning to enjoy living despite life-changing events or chronic illness. I learned that if people feel good about themselves, and are encouraged to be active, interested and social, they heal.

I learned that the process of true healing emanates from deep within the mind and soul and can take place even if 'cure' isn't possible. My interest in the importance of treating the whole person was born.

*　　*　　*

When I returned to the UK, I found clinicians were still treating body parts – knees, hips, backs, hearts – rather than the whole person. Over thirty years later, in the main, this is still the case.

I was able to put my new-found approach into action when I was asked to set up a physiotherapy service in what was then a long-stay geriatric ward. Conditions on the ward, in terms of quality of life, were pretty abysmal for the patients and staff. There was a high incidence of staff ill health and sick days. Their patients were unsurprisingly miserable as they sat padded up with incontinence pads day after day after day around the walls of a large room with the television invariably blaring out. The more mobile among them often found themselves tilted backwards in an attempt to 'keep them safe from falls' which, in turn, rendered them immobile. When we attempted to improve their mobility, unsurprisingly they would scream and hang back with fear. The whole environment was stressful for the staff, patients and their families. The problems went a lot deeper than muscles, joints and balance.

We took the decision to take some significant steps back and began the mobilisation programme by getting to know each individual. Ensuring they had clean clothes and shoes that fitted. We arranged for the women to have access to makeup, if so desired, and for men and women to have regular visits from a hairdresser, chiropodist or manicurist. We rearranged furniture in the dayroom into smaller circles of chairs and then proceeded to give them some structure to each day with a range of activities and interests, including knitting. The TV was switched off, apart from viewing specific programmes chosen beforehand.

Our primary aim became to improve their overall quality of life by helping them to become individuals who engaged with their world once more. We wanted to give back their dignity and pride.

Gradually we began to see a change. Our intervention sparked an interest in their surroundings and the wider world again;

A simple yet powerful solution

they began to talk, take an interest in their appearance, form friendships, talk about their past (many had friends in common), talk about their hobbies, interests and experiences. Continence improved. The ward environment transformed into a pleasant, happy place to be, and as a result, staff sick days dramatically reduced too.

This whole-person approach to health care has informed my clinical practice ever since.

✳   ✳   ✳

Many years later, I observed a similar level of 'isolation' in patients I visited on my community rounds. I was often their only contact with the outside world. Many had pain and a level of disability which made everyday life difficult. Most were profoundly isolated. As a result of the circumstances they found themselves in, most lacked motivation to do anything more than sit all day doing nothing. They had no sense of anticipation or excitement. Their physical and mental inactivity caused secondary problems such as joint stiffness, muscle weakness, poor balance, pain, low social confidence, low self-esteem and low mood. Their days had no structure or purpose. They had nothing in their lives they enjoyed or were successful at. 'Mrs Smith' wasn't getting out of her chair because she had no reason to, and consequently it became more difficult, physically and mentally, for her to do so.

GPs would ask me to assess the issues and teach appropriate exercises to improve mobility but I knew with certainty they

Notes

wouldn't do the exercises I taught or carry out the lifestyle changes I advised.

As with the elderly patients I treated on that long-stay geriatric ward, I felt we needed to take a step back with these patients. They needed to develop an interest in the world, they needed social contact and to develop an aspiration to improve their wellbeing before we had any chance of persuading them to become involved in self-managing their health and wellness.

People need to want to be active before you can succeed in getting them active mentally and physically, so a preliminary stage which stimulates interest, desire and motivation is vital for future successful involvement in managing health and wellness. Those making lifestyle changes also need ongoing support to maintain their interest, desire and motivation. Their willpower and reserves need refuelling.

The system we all found ourselves in wasn't addressing the core problems.

After much soul searching, I left my physiotherapy profession and retrained as a freelance production editor for a range of leisure magazines and found myself working on Future Publishing's craft portfolio. One of my jobs was to look after the letters pages which entailed reading the large volume of mail received every day. I was struck by the high number

A simple yet powerful solution

of people who wrote about the therapeutic benefit of crafts, particularly knitting. Despite coming from different backgrounds and cultures, large numbers of people were making similar comments from around the globe.

Stories told of how getting involved in a project appeared to be changing the mindset of these story writers. Using knitting to distract from pain and life's problems played a small part in this. More significantly, they found something constructive they could succeed at, something that belonged to them, that they had control of. They told of looking forward to their next project, and hence looking forward to the next day, of being motivated again.

Most importantly, they became active, creative participants in life once more.

That was my light-bulb moment – I wondered whether knitting could be used as an activity from the armchair to motivate the people I had seen on my community rounds. To stimulate an interest in the world, to provide safe social contact, to act as a springboard to other activities because this is certainly what the letters were suggesting. That was my starting point – the beginning of Therapeutic Knitting which has since evolved to encompass knitting as a tool for wellness for everyone.

The magazines made it known I was interested in researching the therapeutic benefits of knitting further, so knitters from

Notes

around the world started sending me their stories. It was at this stage I realised I had stumbled across something really exciting, something which could potentially change the way we improve wellbeing and treat long-term medical conditions.

In 2005 I set up Stitchlinks (**www.stitchlinks.com**), which is a global support network for those who enjoy the therapeutic benefits of crafts, particularly knitting. It is also a repository of information for clinicians, teachers and others wishing to learn more about Therapeutic Knitting and a hub for research into those benefits. I wanted users to have easy access to trustworthy information and direct contact with researchers.

Quotes used in this book have been taken from stories sent to Stitchlinks with the contributors' permission – they speak for themselves.

In 2006 I approached the Pain Management Clinic at the Royal United Hospital in Bath, UK, to ask if they would be interested in setting up a social knitting group for their patients. To my surprise they said yes, and the group has been successful on a number of levels in helping those with persistent pain. I have also been using Therapeutic Knitting with people who have complex problems on a one-to-one basis and making progress where other, more conventional approaches have failed.

Healthcare systems around the world are struggling to treat increasing numbers of people and are focusing attention

A simple yet powerful solution

onto the self-management of stress and long-term medical conditions, but their input and ongoing support is frequently inadequate and under resourced.

Through the information I have uncovered, I have learned that the most effective solutions are simple yet powerful, and Therapeutic Knitting is one of these.

I encourage you to approach this book with an open mind and think the issues through intuitively. It's not about getting you to sit all day knitting. On the contrary, it's about a whole-person approach to your wellbeing and using knitting as a tool to improve your health and wellness, whether you are fit and well or suffering ill health. It may be you need to ignite a spark to set you on your way to wellness or need support to enable you to enjoy and maintain that path.

Much of the information is common sense but in our modern, stress-filled world common sense sometimes needs to be voiced more loudly. Some of the information contained will confirm what you may already 'know' in your heart but may not have had the courage to act on.

It represents a different approach to 'being well' and will help you lead a more fulfilling life regardless of your starting point. It will give you a simple yet powerful tool to begin healing and dealing with life any time, anywhere, whether you are fit and well or living with a long-term condition.

A simple yet powerful solution

Notes

The aim of this book is to inspire you to become actively engaged in improving your wellbeing. To this end, make it a book of action by highlighting the points that matter to you. Use the margins and note sections at the end of each chapter to jot down your thoughts, feelings, creative ideas and plans.

Begin your way to wellness by thinking about what you would like this book to help you achieve then write these points down on the opposite page. As you read further, refer back to these goals and refine or change them as necessary.

This book was written with you in mind...

My Goals

1.

2.

3.

4.

5.

My Notes

A simple yet powerful solution

-1-
TAKE
CONTROL
TODAY

Learn how to become proactive

· ·

The brilliant thing about knitting is...
it can enable you to improve your
wellness and put you back in charge...

Notes

Therapeutic Knitting puts power in your hands. It can help you to take control and become involved and proactive in your health and wellness.

The basic approach to achieving wellness should be the same whether you are fit and healthy or have a medical condition. Being involved and active in managing your health and wellness within the wider picture of your life is key to success. Being passive is a passport to ill health and increasing mental, physical and social problems regardless of whether you are currently well or not.

Western medical culture encourages us to expect doctors and healthcare professionals to 'do things to us' – to prescribe a pill for every malady. However, the factors which influence how you feel are so much greater than the issues which can be addressed with medication alone. This 'quick fix' approach has led us to become passive recipients as opposed to active participants in our own wellbeing. This passivity subsequently leads to more problems and prescriptions whereas being actively involved and knowledgeable about your health is empowering. It leads to results whether you are fit and healthy or living with a medical condition and seeking to live a fulfilled life.

Having a tool such as Therapeutic Knitting will enable you to actively engage in improving your health and wellness. Being involved in 'doing' will mean you are more likely to succeed and stay motivated over the longer term.

A simple yet powerful solution

Notes

Wellness isn't about positive thinking or being positive all the time. It is about having the flexibility of mind to deal with any change and challenge life throws your way – actively seeking new experiences, being happy to explore new opportunities with the confidence that any setbacks will provide a valuable learning experience. It's about developing a central core of 'feeling good' despite external influences – where you don't need to depend on good fortune happening to you to feel happy or good about yourself.

Normal life consists of a series of ups and downs, and any approach which focuses solely on living the good bits will fail. Living well is about having the tools to face up to, accept and deal with the inevitable bad experiences and living life to the full despite them. It's about making the most of the good bits and actively seeking to increase your positive experiences. Therapeutic Knitting can help you achieve this.

Change is part of normal life so if you become stressed with every little change in immediate routine or the wider world, your wellness will suffer. In fact, change is the only thing that is certain in life so it is beneficial to view change as offering you an opportunity to improve.

Adopting this viewpoint will enable you to grow, achieve and change. Therapeutic Knitting can help you on this path.

Feeling in control is fundamental to wellness. However, the key lies in being in control and also being flexible.

Notes

On the surface these appear to be contradictory, but by being flexible in the flow of change you also gain control. Being in control in a regime of rigid routines which cannot be broken, particularly if these are combined with perfectionist targets which have to be met, is detrimental to mental and physical health. Strength is in flexibility not rigidity.

Everything you do and experience affects your wellness. A whole-person approach to health and wellness takes into account everything that happens within your life and the context within which you experience everyday challenges.

Your nervous system, including your brain, is an amazing structure which changes with every experience you have. The more you behave in a certain way the more you reinforce and speed up those particular neural pathways so they become strong, habitual superhighways. Thoughts and beliefs are nerve impulses too, so the more you think negatively the more these pathways are strengthened and the more difficult they are to break free from.

External circumstances in life can cause you to behave in certain ways, so too can your thoughts and feelings, thus reinforcing certain behaviours. It can soon become a vicious cycle of downward spiralling, habitual patterns which feed on each other. The more you get trapped in these destructive loops of thought the more negative experiences and fewer positive ones you'll have in life. Therapeutic Knitting can help

A simple yet powerful solution

you to create new positive habits of thinking and behaving which will lead to more positive experiences.

"Knitting helps to train your mind because your mind is occupied concentrating on what you're doing so no negative thoughts can get through."

You may have been taught that your brain has a finite number of brain cells which gradually die away as you age. This is a depressing thought which is entirely false. The development of detailed brain scanning has enabled scientists to discover that new brain cells can be generated in certain areas and new neural pathways can be opened and strengthened even into old age providing you take action to ensure this happens.

Whatever your starting point, you CAN make progress. You CAN increase those positive moments in life.

That's an exciting future to anticipate and Therapeutic Knitting can help you achieve this.

There is a body of thought which believes that the more neural pathways you have functioning the less likely you are to experience the symptoms of dementia or other destructive brain disease. Evidence from autopsies of highly intelligent people appears to confirm this viewpoint – some of the brains examined showed extensive damage consistent with dementia yet there was no evidence of symptoms in these people when they were alive. It seems logical to me that the

Notes

Notes

more you have, the more reserve you have available should you run into problems.

As with muscles, it's a question of 'using it or losing it'. These brain changes are reversible, which is good news if you are working towards changing more negative aspects but it does mean that this proactive approach needs to be a long-term lifestyle choice. Crucially, we know that if you sit unoccupied the brain declines, so it's highly beneficial to continue enjoying learning new skills and maintaining social networks in order to preserve and improve your brain health.

Psychologists over the years have studied human needs from the basics required to simply stay alive through to satisfying the more highly evolved, developed functions needed to ensure we live fulfilled lives. The American psychologist Abraham Maslow developed a ladder of human needs known as Maslow's Hierarchy, which is traditionally illustrated in the form of a triangle or pyramid. The most basic needs that keep us alive – food, shelter, water – are the first layer to satisfy. Next comes safety, which includes security of body, health, family and employment, followed by love and belonging then esteem. At the pinnacle of the pyramid lies self-actualisation – the need to reach your full potential, to excel, to be fully alive. This covers morality, creativity, spontaneity, problem solving and acceptance of facts. Maslow stated that to reach your full potential, the issues at the base of the triangle need to be addressed – a man whose very survival depends on finding food, water and shelter has no time or interest in exploring the creative side of life. Survival takes precedence.

The Human Givens organisation believes that human beings come into the world with a set of needs which, if appropriately met, leads to wellbeing and good mental health. They have identified 'meaning', 'purpose', 'sense of volition and control', 'being needed by others', 'having intimate connections and wider social connections', 'status' and 'appropriate giving and receiving attention' as being crucial for health and wellbeing.

The influential occupational therapist Ann Wilcock recognised the human need for occupation and identified a range of positive influences on health plus risk factors which could affect wellbeing. She listed the positive effects as satisfaction, creativity, meaning and purpose, having challenges to meet, the importance of belonging and sharing and of having social value and a sense of community. Of those issues having a negative influence on health, she lists alienation, deprivation, imbalance and lack of opportunity to develop.

These approaches illustrate how your environment and your level of knowledge can affect your health and why a whole-person approach to wellbeing and health care is so important.

Therapeutic Knitting on your own and in safe, supportive social groups will give you an accessible tool to change these issues. It will enable you to lay firm foundations from which you can deal with life's challenges to improve your wellbeing.

Notes

Your brain has a circuit called the reward system – it fires off a boost of feel-good chemicals when you are successful at tasks which require a little effort. Professor Kelly Lambert theorises that depression has its roots in the decline of this circuit. If you don't use it, you lose it.[2,3]

The narratives I have been collecting since 2005 tell a similar story. I have become intrigued by how some people live fulfilled lives despite numerous setbacks, problems or ill health, whereas others sink under seemingly minor issues.

Five issues come up time and time again –

• Social isolation and loneliness
• Worry, fear, stress
• Lack of rewarding occupation
• Low self-esteem, confidence and feelings of worthlessness
• Changed or lost identity.

I will discuss these in more detail in following chapters, but you can see they are much along the same lines as the issues Maslow, Human Givens and Wilcock highlight. They tend to feed on each other and produce physical symptoms such as muscle tension, poor posture, bowel symptoms, pain and sleep problems, to name but a few. The symptoms, in turn, feed back into this cycle to create destructive loops of thought and patterns of behaviour. Therapeutic Knitting can help you to deal with all these issues and break into negative thought cycles.

A simple yet powerful solution

It's difficult to enjoy life to the full or be well if these issues aren't dealt with. Variety is key to living a fulfilled life, but the very variety and change that makes life so interesting can pose huge problems for many. All of us will experience one or more of these core issues at some stage – perhaps you are shy, newly retired, elderly, a teenager experiencing change, divorcing, a carer, naturally introverted or in a rut with life. There are many benefits to being consciously active in recognising and dealing with them.

If you are currently fit and well, ensuring these issues are addressed will enable you to maintain that inner 'feel-good core'. If you are struggling to manage ill health, taking steps to address them alongside medical treatments will enable a whole-person approach to your health and wellbeing. It is my opinion that no matter how good the biological approach to treatment may be, problems will recur if you don't consider, and act on, this bigger picture. Current healthcare systems seldom take into account the 'other factors' that influence the way we feel – the context within which we experience health or suffer ill health, but it is in your power to take action to do just that. It will significantly influence how you react, manage or recover.

> *"What started as a way of dealing with the problems*
> *in my life has brought healing in so many ways.*
> *It kept me calm amid my greatest fears and anxieties;*
> *it nourished me with its colours and textures.*
> *It is empowerment.*

A simple yet powerful solution

Notes

Notes

"In the long term, knitting restored my broken confidence in self and the world.

"It was something to cling to in the darkest moments, a raft."

Therapeutic Knitting can help you to break free from the passivity, problems and prescriptions cycle. As part of a holistic approach to health, Therapeutic Knitting can enable you to influence your bodymind and spirit, change your home and social environment, as well as complement any medical treatment you may be receiving.

You CAN make positive change happen but it will only do so from within you, not as a result of someone or something else doing something to you.

Successful change requires perseverance to develop new habits while ensuring you keep your reserves and willpower replenished. Using knitting as a portable tool will enable you to take positive action any time, anywhere. The Stitchlinks website will provide ongoing friendship, information and support to keep your reserves and willpower refuelled and set you on your way to wellness.

It is exciting to know that by becoming involved and taking action you CAN improve your life, and knitting can enable you to start today. Take small steps, keep at it and the benefits will come.

A simple yet powerful solution

Identify what you would like to achieve, write it down and use the combination of this book and Therapeutic Knitting to empower you to succeed.

Take a little time to review the goals you wrote at the start of this book and make changes to them if necessary.

Make a decision to take control today to improve your health and wellness and reach your pinnacle of potential.

Notes

POINTS TO PERUSE

1. Use knitting and this book to gain knowledge and a tool. Getting involved and 'doing' will help you succeed, while keeping you motivated along that path and refuelling your reserves. Stick at it and the benefits will come.

2. Practise being flexible in your thinking and keep practising – it is fundamental to being well. It will enable you to stay in control. Strength lies in flexibility not rigidity.

3. Develop a central feel-good core despite external influences. Focus on taking pleasure from each moment and the things you have easy access to.

4. Adopt a whole-person approach to your health and wellbeing by taking into account the influence of everything that happens in your life and reviewing its effect.

Notes

5. Remember, the factors which influence how you feel are so much greater than the issues which can be addressed with medication alone. Attend to those Core Issues.

6. Be proactive in your health and wellness. Use Therapeutic Knitting as a tool. It will help you to break free from the 3 Ps – passivity, problems and prescriptions. It may not be easy at first but use your knitting to keep at it.

7. Take action to keep your brain healthy and vibrant. Remember if you don't use it, you'll lose it. Learn and keep learning new skills throughout your life.

8. Make positive change happen today. However small, make a start, take that first, small step. It can only happen from within you, not as a result of someone doing something to you.

Notes

My Notes

A simple yet powerful solution

-2-
WHAT MAKES KNITTING SPECIAL?

Discover the potential in your hands

· ·

The brilliant thing about knitting is…

it puts portable power

in your hands…

Notes

My work has involved looking behind the art of knitting and providing scientific explanations for what knitters across the globe are saying. What I have uncovered is exciting and makes knitting special.

In terms of getting the world of Science interested in my work, the word 'knitting' has been the biggest barrier. At face value, knitting and science seem worlds apart... until now.

What actually goes on behind the 'K' word is complex and exciting in many ways.

To get my foot in the door with scientists, academics and clinicians I began by calling knitting 'a bilateral, rhythmic, psychosocial intervention'. It is a phrase that grabbed their attention and interest.

Any activity you enjoy which is not harmful to others will benefit your sense of wellbeing, but knitting has some special qualities which make it stand out from the crowd.
These are –

• The hand movements
• The hand position
• The way it enables eye contact... or not
• Its portability.

Anthropological evidence suggests hand movements and function cause the brain to develop in certain ways.

A simple yet powerful solution

Our actions and movements are reflected in maps within our brains. Knitting maps will be regularly reinforced because most knitters knit three to five times a week, while many knit every day.

The information you get from your hands is also important in helping to build your personal 'picture of the world'. What you perceive as 'reality' is actually a complex construction by your brain of all the sensory information it gathers and processes subconsciously every split second.

"Our hands help us to develop a sense of self by telling us where our body ends and the rest of the world begins."
Professor Leah Krubitzer.

As a physiotherapist specialising in neurological treatments, I was immediately interested in the nature of the movements and their potential impact on the brain. Physiotherapists have been using bilateral patterns of movement for the treatment of brain injury for years.

We tend to believe the information our brain gives us... but sometimes it comes to the wrong conclusions. Habitual behaviours or long-term illness can change your perception of the world – physically and psychologically. Those with long-term pain, for example, often have an altered perception of space. This can vary from limbs that feel a different shape or size to not being able to accurately gauge the space their body occupies. Similarly someone who is normally housebound can feel very unsafe in an open or crowded environment. The brain's perception of reality isn't necessarily always accurate.

With this in mind, my interest in the two-handed nature of the movements increased when knitters with long-term pain made comments such as –

> *"It's strange, I feel like I know where I am in space."*

> *"I've noticed I can walk around the supermarket without feeling like I'm going to bump into things."*

> *"I can walk down the busy street and not bump into people – I seem to 'know' where I am."*

Knitting involves a complex bilateral, coordinated pattern of movements. This will require a lot of integration in your brain to fine tune the movements to enable your hands to work together in a precise way, which means your brain will be working quite hard.

The fact that these movements cross the midline of the body is interesting too – cross midline movements take up even more brain capacity.

The midline of the body is a significant reference point for the brain. Research is at an early stage but crossing the midline can affect your perception of pain in a limb, for example[4]. It's not fully understood why.

A simple yet powerful solution

Performing a bilateral, coordinated pattern of movement across the midline of the body that you're also looking at is a complicated process – it uses up a lot of brain capacity leaving it with less capacity to pay attention to other issues. Add in some counting plus an intricate knitting pattern and you use even more. A large number of narratives collected from knitters describe knitting as highly effective in distracting the brain's attention, and you can take advantage of this to take control of your life.

Getting down to the nitty-gritty of the movements does raise the thorny issue of whether throwing your yarn in a larger movement across the midline may prove to be more beneficial than the smaller movements of continental knitting.

*   *   *

Whatever your style of knitting, the movements are also important in other ways.

Studies in animals have shown that repetitive movement enhances the release of serotonin[5, 6]. Serotonin raises mood but it also calms and is an analgesic. People often instinctively engage in repetitive, rhythmic movement when they are stressed or traumatised. They are intuitively self-soothing as they rock, pace or tap.

Frequent knitting (more than three times a week) can help people feel calmer and happier, even those suffering from clinical depression[1].

A simple yet powerful solution

Notes

In our Stitchlinks / Cardiff University study[1], respondents often attributed the feeling of calm to the rhythmic nature of the movements and spoke of entering a meditative-like state and 'zoning out' or being 'in the zone'. Numerous narratives also support this.

*"I can actually feel all the tension just fade out of me.
I become totally focused on the rhythm of my
hands and I can just let go of everything
I've been carrying around all day."*

This rhythm is important because knitters control it and change it according to their mood at a particular moment. If you are forced to knit at a rhythm which is out of sync with your natural inclinations of the moment, it can make you feel stressed. Those knitting to unrealistically tight or rigid deadlines often report this.

The rhythm of the movements facilitates a sense of deep calm and the meditative-like state so widely attributed to knitting. It is instantaneously familiar and comforting, which together with the portability, gives you a powerful tool for managing stress, panic and anxiety anywhere. From a therapeutic viewpoint, this has many practical applications and I will talk about this in Chapter 10.

The calming effects enable knitters to enjoy the process as much as achieving the end result. This ongoing reward, which doesn't rely on an end product, is motivating. It encourages

A simple yet powerful solution

persistence which is necessary for successful change to occur. Respondents to the Stitchlinks / Cardiff University study told us that knitting helped them to develop skills of persistence, patience and planning[1].

Enjoying the moment and process in this way gives the brain a break from worrying thoughts about the past or future. It is often described as enjoying the sanctuary of a quiet mind.

Regular meditation is known to have numerous benefits for health[7, 8]. It can reduce inflammation, induce healing, encourage positive outlook and even help you grow new neural pathways and brain cells. Unfortunately, the people who need it the most (the stressed or ill) are often those who find it the most difficult to learn – stressful thoughts or symptoms can all too easily encroach on the meditative state.

Entering a meditative-like state appears to happen as a natural side effect of knitting.

This has the potential to open up the benefits of meditation to a wider audience – the elderly, learning disabled, children – without them having to accept or understand the underlying concepts, or engage in an involved learning process. New knitters can begin to get into the flow of the movements quite quickly and they soon become automatic.

The automatic nature of the movements may be important in other ways. Rumination describes powerful loops of habitual,

Notes

negative thought cycles which become trapped in your subconscious and difficult to break. Automatic movement maps are stored in your subconscious – like driving a car or riding a bike, you perform them without having to think consciously about each component.

Knitters report knitting as having the power to break into, and push out, cycles of rumination, so the automatic nature of the movements could be playing an important part in refocusing the mind onto more positive, forward-thinking thought processes. Therapeutically, the prospect that performing automatic movements could help us to access the subconscious has huge potential.

Automatic movement can also help to initiate and encourage movement of the hands if you have hand problems. This is particularly the case if you have knitted before. You may need a small reminder, but generally, once learned, the 'knitting know how' will be with you for life.

It has been my observation that when the brain is occupied with a background automatic task, conversation tends to get deeper and more intimate. Narratives from knitters who enjoy knitting in groups support this. It is as if the background attention paid to knitting takes up just enough brain capacity to 'switch off' self-monitoring. This can be useful if you are naturally shy or introverted as you will find yourself joining in with and enjoying conversations happening around you. In a therapeutic setting, it is useful

A simple yet powerful solution

for encouraging those who have low social confidence or find it difficult to talk.

"Conversations tend to be more intimate and/or involving than they would generally be. It's almost as if the repetitive motions allow for the barriers of self to drop and conversation becomes easier."

If you attend a knitting group you will know that loud laughter and easy banter are hallmarks of people who gather together to knit. The rhythmic, automatic movements encourage the feeling of relaxation, familiarity and comfort, which in turn encourages laughter, fun and conversation.

The nature of knitting's movements may also be affecting the symptoms of post traumatic stress disorder (PTSD). Knitters suffering from this condition report a reduction in incidence of flashbacks and other symptoms such as nightmares.

Emily Holmes and Catherine Deeprose at Oxford University in the UK have studied the effect of visuo-spatial movement on the incidence of flashbacks. They found that performing a repetitive visuo-spatial movement during or immediately following a traumatic event significantly reduced frequency of flashbacks. The study advised these movements be performed within a six hour window of the trauma and recommended that further studies be done on knitting and worry beads[9,10].

Notes

Notes

Knitters, however, report an improvement in PTSD symptoms way beyond a six-hour time frame. It could be that deliberately activating a traumatic memory whilst performing the visuo-spatial movement of knitting has the same effect.

*   *   *

I have no doubt that the combination of movement, thought and feeling is important. I would describe it as unifying.

"I think that for me the whole process is a way of reconnecting myself back together again."

It has been my observation that those who are psychologically stressed or suffering from unmanaged, long-term medical problems often appear 'fractured'. When you are well, your mind and body work in harmony as bodymind, and as a result you flow along with seemingly little effort, oblivious of the millions of interactions occurring throughout your being. However, when problems arise your attention is drawn to areas which become accentuated by the attention. You may also become aware of a constant chitter-chatter going on in the background which is disruptive to wellbeing. Disharmony develops and appears to fracture the healthy body mind relationship, bringing it to the forefront of your attention.

The combination of rhythmic movement, thought and feeling appears to calm this conflict. It is somehow integrating – Yoga and T'ai Chi are examples of activities which also appear to have this unifying effect.

A simple yet powerful solution

The neurologist Frank Wilson puts it well in his book, The Hand[11] –

> *"When personal desire prompts anyone to learn to do something well with the hands, an extremely complicated process is initiated that endows the work with a powerful emotional charge. People are changed significantly and irreversibly it seems, when movement, thought and feeling fuse during active, long-term pursuit of personal goals."*

*   *   *

The position of your hands as you knit is also important – it increases your personal space to give the perception of increased safety.

Many narratives talk about the hand position providing a buffer to the outside world. In combination with the calming, self-soothing properties, this can be used to manage a range of situations, particularly if you have a tendency to be anxious in social situations or on public transport.

Some psychologists would argue that giving you a tool to manage situations where you are fearful doesn't help you face those fears – it merely helps you avoid them. I would argue that everyone needs a little help to be successful when taking that first, important step, otherwise you may never take it. Knitting can provide you with that springboard. From there your confidence will grow. Stories tell of moving on to

Notes

not having to use knitting to calm anxiety or panic after a while – the knowledge that you have a simple yet powerful solution in your bag is enough.

Many knitters use their craft to enable them to socialise, use public transport or attend a therapeutic group. Without it they would never have taken that vital first step.

"It is not escapism, but I am able in the knitterly moments
(knitting, and planning, and choosing, and imagining)
to separate myself from the concerns of the moment."

✳ ✳ ✳

Knitting is also one of the few activities which enables eye contact as you chat... or not.

The 'or not' is important because it puts YOU in complete control. It makes it perfectly acceptable to sit and knit quietly if you so desire. Therapeutically this is important because it will encourage you to join a group and keep attending even if you're feeling vulnerable.

Knitting not only enables those first steps in socialisation but it enables people to access the therapeutic groups they may need and encourages you to stick at it.

✳ ✳ ✳

Knitting is one of the few truly portable activities. Being easily accessible, portable and conducive to group and individual

A simple yet powerful solution

environments means knitters have a powerful tool at hand any time, anywhere.

Knitting as a therapeutic activity also meets other important criteria when considering an activity suitable for a range of different environments including clinical ones. It isn't messy, it is easily accessible to all and cuts across class, culture, background and educational status so anyone can benefit. The activity itself can be learned or reinforced from books, DVDs and YouTube so there is plenty of support available between group sessions. It is also a cost effective means of learning because work can be undone as you experiment and explore different stitch combinations.

The combination of knitting's movements, hand position, portability and the way it enables eye contact, or not, make it special.

Discovering this potential in your hands will enable you to take your life in hand.

Knowing you have portable power at your fingertips can be life affirming. It's your helping hand to wellness...

Notes

POINTS TO PERUSE

1. Focus on the information and feeling you get from your hands while you knit. It will help you to build your personal picture of the world.

2. Look at your hands while you knit if you want to distract your brain from problems or negative issues. It will take up a lot of brain capacity, leaving less available for other issues.

3. Knit more than three times a week. It will help you to feel calmer and happier, even if you suffer from clinical depression.

4. Focus on the rhythm and repetitive nature of the movements. It will enable you to enjoy the sanctuary of a quiet mind.

Notes

5. Become absorbed in the process of knitting. The ongoing feel-good reward will motivate you on your way to wellness.

6. Experience the unifying effect of Therapeutic Knitting. Become engrossed in the combination of movement, thought and feeling.

7. Use the automatic movements of knitting to enable conversation to flow more easily if you're naturally shy or anxious in the company of others.

8. Choose to look at people as you knit and chat... or not. Don't be afraid to sit and knit quietly, it's perfectly acceptable. This will put you in control in group situations.

Notes

My Notes

A simple yet powerful solution

-3-
KNIT
TO
BENEFIT

Win, and help others win too

· ·

The brilliant thing about knitting is...

everyone wins...

Notes

The knowledge gathered in this book will help you to make personal gains as well as benefit your relationships, friendships, leisure, working experiences and even people you have never met.

However you choose to knit (for the process or product), whoever you choose to knit for (yourself, friends, family or charity), there are benefits for all involved. You can knit to benefit your own health and give gifts to benefit others at the same time. So let's take a look at how you can win and help others to win too.

As part of your whole-person approach to health and wellness, you'll find it beneficial to consider your general mood, thinking patterns, levels of self-esteem and stress as well as how much you engage in social, creative and rewarding activities and occupations. They all impact on your health and wellness in significant ways.

If you are fit and healthy, using knitting as a tool will enable you to deal with the normal stresses and strains of everyday life. This will help to prevent future problems arising. It will also enable you to manage those unplanned for scenarios and life's more stressful, but inevitable events.

If you suffer from ill health, your knitting can enable you to improve your wellbeing and enjoy a fuller life. It can help you to manage symptoms, cut down on medication, enjoy social situations and give gifts. It can give you back control.

A simple yet powerful solution

Notes

"I concentrate on the knitting in my hands as the yarn coils itself around my hand and works its way along the needles. It's a way to take back control of my mind when the situation I am in is not conducive to meditation."

In our Stitchlinks / Cardiff University study[1], knitters reported their reasons for knitting are the therapeutic, meditative, relaxing qualities as well as being productive and enabling contribution through gift giving and charity work. Being 'creative' is also seen as an important benefit along with enabling social interaction and making friends. So whatever your aim, be it one or all of the above, you can begin to benefit today and help others along the way.

"Knitting enables free-flowing and restorative thought. If ever I am feeling stressed or low I reach for my needles and am soon feeling uplifted. Knitting enables me to channel my emotions into the garment I am creating, and helps turn negative emotions round to positive ones."

Quiet knitting (see Chapter 4) will provide you with a means for relaxation, calm and enjoyment of solitude.

Attending a knitting group (see Chapter 5) will enable you to meet others in a safe, social environment to enjoy fun, laughter and easy banter in the company of others.

A knitting group will enable you to belong to a supportive community. A group local to you will help to create and build

Notes

a strong local community as well as gain access to a range of interesting people from diverse backgrounds.

Knitting can help you manage everyday life, manage change, deal with normal fluctuations in mood, keep your stress at a healthy level, occupy you during boring journeys or otherwise unproductive time and help you to sleep better. It can literally change your mind and how you feel about yourself, your life and the world.

"Knitting has enabled me to challenge my own stereotypes about myself. I can't be useless if I can knit even a simple scarf. My concentration can't be that bad if I can knit lace and socks and complicated patterns."

Knitting can be really valuable for relaxing or unwinding after work, and our study found that this was particularly important for those whose work involved sitting at computers. Switching from 2D screen-based work to a 3D tactile, creative task helps to manage the stresses of the day and gives your brain a completely different focus. It can also occupy you on your commute to work, and a bit of lunch break knitting can help you to manage stress, meet new people and improve your creative thinking and problem solving.

It is possible to remember and recall the feelings of calm you experience during knitting and use this to help in most situations you are fearful of. This works even when you don't have your knitting to hand or when the situation may not be

A simple yet powerful solution

conducive to knitting, such as during an exam, an interview or public speaking.

Purposeful occupation is known to be beneficial for wellbeing – it provides structure and purpose to each day. However, this work has highlighted the importance of making a distinction between dutiful, purposeful occupation and rewarding, purposeful occupation – activities that fire off that reward system. I'm talking about the jobs you feel duty-bound to do versus the activities you enjoy.

Housework, for example, is purposeful but you may not find it enjoyable, particularly if you're feeling unwell. Many of those who suffer ill health and low self-esteem prioritise household chores over activities for their own wellbeing. They do this because they feel guilty at not being able to contribute to life or to their family in other ways, particularly if their condition has necessitated giving up work. As a result, life becomes a list of chores and ill health. Their attention is focused more on getting through the basics of life rather than enjoying creative activities which enable them to experience their full potential – finding self-actualisation, reaching their personal pinnacle of potential.

Being able to think creatively is important for wellbeing, your ability to think flexibly and problem solving. It opens up more options and ideas. Thinking creatively can also act as an ongoing distraction.

Notes

You can use your knitting to deliberately nurture your creative ability. This can help you to manage change, think innovatively, problem solve more effectively and better self-manage work issues and life in general as well as any symptoms of illness you may be experiencing. Thinking creatively can become a beneficial habit which can occupy your mind and distract it from negative issues or symptoms such as pain in a more sustained, positive, ongoing way.

"The buzz that I get from the creating is the potent drive."

Creativity is what sets us humans apart. It is the wellspring of wellness.

Thinking and behaving in a flexible way will enable you to respond in a way which doesn't lead you to think negatively or catastrophically when enforced life changes occur. A flexible mind is able to 'ride the flow' of change. Being able to think creatively will expand your options and enable you to respond in more resourceful, innovative ways. You can develop your creative ability through knitting and I talk more about this in Chapter 10.

Knitting will enable you to lower your stress levels whilst developing creative thought and enjoying social contact, making it an effective enabling tool.

Having goals to aim for gives purpose to life. Knitting teaches the skills of appropriate goal setting. It's important to set

Notes

flexible goals because sometimes life gets in the way or unforeseen opportunities arise. It's about being flexible at the same time as knowing your direction in life.

I encourage people to take 'purposeful pathways' rather than 'rigid routes' because the aim of life is to enjoy as many moments as you can along the paths you take. A goal will give you direction but sometimes you may find it is necessary to divert from the path to encompass or allow for external influences and explore opportunities. Knitting will teach you that, with perseverance, you can still reach your goal despite a few detours along the way – like a river flowing to the sea.

Life is a collection of moments and if you focus too much on the end goal, you can miss those moments – miss the moments and you will miss out on life.

Knitting visually reflects the ethos of breaking tasks down, of taking one step at a time – each stitch you make represents a successful step towards the end of the row and each row is a step towards your goal, be that enjoyment of the process or knitting a gift.

Enforced change, in the form of illness, redundancy, retirement or old age can affect your feelings of self-worth and change your identity – the person you feel you are. Feeling able to contribute is important in creating your identity and status in society, so when this is affected it's easy to feel lost and

Notes

insignificant. Not knowing who or where you are in the world is highly detrimental to wellbeing.

Knitting can be used to make gifts, to contribute to your family and, through charities and other causes, to contribute to wider society and help others win too. The act of giving can greatly ease the burden of feeling worthless. It can help you to create a new, positive identity. Research has shown that giving to charity boosts feel-good chemicals in your brain[12]. The Stitchlinks / Cardiff University study[1] showed that the making and giving of gifts was a significant reason for knitting. The recipient receives a hand-knitted gift and the knitter gets a boost of feel-good chemicals as well as finding a niche in the world. Everyone wins!

"There are many times when I feel like
I serve no purpose to anyone
and then I am reminded of the blankets,
sweaters and stitched pieces I have made
for others. It is a great picker upper."

The knitting world also has many 'causes' to knit for. For example, you could knit socks for soldiers, chemo hats for cancer sufferers, blankets for the elderly, baby clothes for premature babies or sick children in Africa, hats for the homeless or blankets for stray dogs and cats, to name but a few. The 'Prayer Shawl Ministry' encourages knitters to knit shawls for abused women and the shawls are sent as a hug from a stranger. There have even been knitted petitions such

A simple yet powerful solution

as the 'Knit a River Campaign' organised by I Knit[13] and Water Aid in the UK.

There is something powerfully symbolic about wrapping a vulnerable person in something warm and cosy, and the knowledge that you have improved a life will improve your life too.

Knitting for those in more need than yourself can dramatically change your perspective on life. It can subtly change your thinking – you become aware that you have the ability and power to improve the lives of those worse off than yourself, and in so doing, your own. This knowledge can help you to build a new identity based on positive feelings and actions.

"Knitting has given me hope and a true belief in me. Even though others have always believed me to be capable of doing anything I wanted, I have always doubted that, and knitting has somehow encouraged me otherwise."

The benefits of contributing and feeling worthwhile in your immediate family, community or wider society go far deeper than that initial feel-good boost. It connects you to that group or community giving you a sense of belonging – and we all need to 'belong' somewhere. It helps to build an inner sense of 'who you are in society'. By developing a strong core of self-belief, you can learn to 'know who YOU are' despite external pressures. Those who retain a strong sense of who they are tend to manage any long-term health condition

Notes

more effectively because they remain separated from their disease. They don't 'become' their illness.

The human brain can only focus on one thing at a time, and although some of us think we can multi-task effectively, your brain is actually switching rapidly between different tasks and not performing any as efficiently as when a single task is the sole focus of attention. The good news is you can use this fact to your advantage. If you find your mind is focused on negative thoughts or issues detrimental to your wellbeing, it is possible to distract your brain's attention away from those problems by deliberately giving it an absorbing knitting task to focus on.

Having the knowledge and a tool to distract your mind from problems or symptoms of ill health can give you power and put you back in control. Feeling in control will significantly change your outlook on life.

It gets even better. There is a lot more going on than simple distraction during the actual process of knitting. There is an ongoing refocusing of attention. You will find yourself planning and thinking about knitting and future projects when you're not actually knitting. You will plan what to knit, who to knit for and the colours and textures you might use. You will imagine how those textures feel and how the colours will impact the completed design. If the project is to be a gift, you will think of the pleasure your gift will bring and the

A simple yet powerful solution

praise you will receive not only when the gift is opened but every time it is worn or used.

There are numerous benefits for you. The whole process focuses your mind on positive, forward thinking, constructive events and feelings, which encourages positive thinking, imagination, visualisation and creativity. The process stirs emotions and feelings of anticipation, pride, excitement and happiness, which if you've been feeling unwell or stressed, you may not have experienced for some time. This will help to change thought patterns by diverting attention away from, and breaking, any negative, destructive cycles.

The more you use these positive pathways, the stronger they become. In this way you establish positive habits and begin to change the very neural pathways that make up your brain to literally change your mind.

Feeling successful is empowering. Believing you CAN do something will make you feel good.

*   *   *

Having fun and enjoying play are important aspects of living well, particularly if you are in the company of others who are supportive and encouraging. Fun and play can so easily be squeezed out of our daily lives as we strive to work longer hours and achieve unattainable goals. It can also be difficult to have fun if you're feeling unwell, so having an activity which distracts from problems at the same time as calming

Notes

Notes

anxieties and encouraging laughter can be an effective means of introducing fun back into your life.

The volume of laughter which emanates from a knitting group is noticeable and, of course, laughter is beneficial in its own right. Even the act of smiling has been shown to raise mood and make you feel better.

Knitting's portability plays a crucial role in its success as a tool for wellness, making it an activity you CAN succeed at from your armchair or anywhere else.

This easy accessibility is a powerful motivator which will encourage you to progress, to learn more and to explore and experiment with new creative ideas.

Your self-esteem and confidence will get a huge boost from 'seeing' progress, feeling successful and being able to contribute to others.

Knitting's portability enables all these benefits to be available to you any time, anywhere making it an ideal tool for improving wellness wherever and whenever you please – in bed, at home, on the commute to work, in the pub with your friends, standing in queues, when you're angry, sad or simply want some time to yourself.

Whether you knit purely for the calming effects of the process or for the end product, you can knit to benefit your own health and wellbeing as well as giving gifts to benefit others. Everyone wins.

It's your powerful, purposeful path to wellness.

Have patience with yourself, stick at it and you WILL do it.

You CAN win and help others to win too.

Notes

POINTS TO PERUSE

1. Knit to benefit your own wellbeing and create gifts to benefit others at the same time. It will feel good.

2. Keep your stress levels under control with a daily dose of knitting. It will greatly benefit your health and wellbeing as well as help to prevent future problems.

3. Get into the habit of thinking creatively. It will expand your options and enable you to respond in more resourceful, innovative ways in all aspects of your life.

4. Know your direction in life but be flexible. Set purposeful pathways rather than rigid routes and break them down into achievable steps. Remember to enjoy each moment along the way.

Notes

A simple yet powerful solution

5. Make a distinction between dutiful, purposeful occupation and activities that make you feel good. The jobs you feel duty-bound to do versus the activities you enjoy.

6. Use your knitting to break destructive negative thought cycles. Focus your mind on positive, forward thinking constructive experiences. It is all about increasing those positive moments.

7. Give to others. It will make you feel good, help you to build a strong core of self-belief, build a positive identity and help them too.

8. Knit for people in more need than yourself. You have the power to improve their lives and change your perspective on the world at the same time. You CAN help someone else.

Notes

My Notes

A simple yet powerful solution

-4-
QUIET
KNITTING

Achieve inner peace and learn to relish solitude

• •

The brilliant thing about knitting is...

you don't have to depend on others.

The power is in your hands...

Notes

The brilliant thing about quiet knitting is that you can do it in the company of your family, with your cat or dog by your side, or in the peace of your own presence – it doesn't require any special setting or organisation. You have a helping hand available any time of night or day.

Change is a normal part of life. It is essential for introducing the variety you need to truly thrive but it can often be stressful. Using your knitting as a self-soothing tool will ease the passage of life's challenges and enable you to embrace change as offering new opportunities and experiences.

Quiet knitting provides you with a tool to manage your day-to-day wellbeing, to ride the flow of life's inevitable challenges and change.

Modern lifestyles are insidiously stressful and difficult to switch off from, so stress can build silently in the background to levels which will affect your health, relationships and wellbeing in many ways. It is therefore valuable to set aside some time each day to relax and experience the sanctuary of a peaceful mind in order to lower your levels of stress and enable your body's natural healing system to kick in. Your knitting can enable you to achieve this.

"I use my knitting as a place, a hobby all mine and just for me. A place I can be meditative and just feel the structure of the yarn and the almost hypnotic click-clack of the needles. Knitting helps me heal."

A simple yet powerful solution

Stress is a major source of health problems in modern life. It is a powerful state of bodymind in which high levels of stress hormones are pumped throughout your body to maximise a state of 'fight or flight'. This can get you out of immediate danger but, over the longer term, stress is highly destructive to every system and organ in your body. Getting your stress levels under control on a daily basis is paramount to improving your health and wellbeing.

"Within a row, I could feel the muscles in my neck loosen up and my body began relaxing for the first time in months. I could almost feel my brain unkinking itself, realising that it wasn't all that bad and calming down."

The state of stress evolved to help early humans stand and fight or run from danger. The stress 'fight or flight' response equipped the body with the necessary strength and energy to get out of danger, whether that was standing to fight or out-running the source of threat. There are many stories of superhuman feats being performed during times of high danger – it is your stress system that makes those possible.

Under threatening circumstances, a surge of stress hormones ensures your heart is pumping more blood to your muscles, taking oxygen to fuel muscle cells and transporting waste products away. Your brain will be more alert and ready to react. During this process, the blood supply to your digestive and reproductive systems will be significantly reduced to enable a focus on systems which will get you out of danger.

Notes

Notes

You will become 'wired' for 'fight or flight' action. A body in this state doesn't sleep, digest or reproduce – these become secondary functions to survival. This is why those in a constant state of chronic stress have problems sleeping, digesting and conceiving.

It is a complex survival mechanism which has evolved to keep you alive in specific situations. The very action of fighting or running, under these circumstances, will dissipate those high levels of stress hormones. These days, however, in 'normal' everyday life you have little call to stand and fight or run for your life. In modern society the problem of stress is much more insidious and ongoing. Your stress response can be triggered by a slamming door, loud noise, high workload, bullying boss, the commute to work – in fact, any number of issues which, although unpleasant, are not directly life threatening. However, they can become so as a result of long-term unmanaged stress.

In modern-day life those stress hormones aren't naturally dissipated, so unless you actively do something to relax on a daily basis you will be stacking up levels of stress chemicals which eventually become destructive to health.

We all need a certain level of pressure to keep motivated, stimulated and interested in life, but ongoing, uncontrolled levels are highly dangerous to health and wellbeing. They also prevent your body's natural healing system from doing its job.

A simple yet powerful solution

It is not known why the stress system has remained little changed down the evolutionary path but one viewpoint is that modern life has changed faster than the human body is able to evolve. However, perhaps it is too important a survival mechanism to warrant changing because there are still times in life when humans may need this basic survival response.

*　　*　　*

In our Stitchlinks / Cardiff University study[1], knitters quoted the rhythmic movements of knitting, and the meditative-like calming feeling these movements induce, as a major reason for daily knitting. We found that there was a significant relationship between the frequency of knitting and feeling calm – the more often people knitted, the calmer they were likely to feel.

Knitting is a great way of unwinding and keeping your stress at a healthy level.

Setting aside 20 minutes a day to engage in the quiet rhythmic process of knitting can help to manage the daily levels of stress we are all subject to. Being able to 'switch off' for a period of time every day is important for your health and wellbeing, particularly in this age of 24/7 internet access. Your body needs time to heal, grow and recuperate and this does not take place when your body is 'wired' to fight or fly – healing becomes secondary to survival. It is beneficial for us all to have a quiet period of down time and mind rest every day.

Notes

Notes

*"It is so meditative.
I sit and knit and am lost in my own quiet world."*

Your body cannot be on alert the whole time without suffering the consequences of being in this permanent state of stress. A body in this state does not heal, digest, sleep or reproduce. It can lead to conditions such as irritable bowel, chronic pain, fibromyalgia, chronic fatigue, heart disease, even cancer. Managing stress on a regular basis is vital for your health and wellness.

This state of stress is triggered automatically – speed is essential to protect us from danger – but the state of relaxation must be deliberately sought so you need to be proactive in making this happen.

It is important to 'escape' from switched on, high tech lifestyles on a regular, daily basis. If you are in a stressful job, take a moment during your lunch break to 'knit and switch off'. You'll find doing this will be beneficial in many ways, it could even help you solve that problem you've been mulling over all morning – if you take your focus off a problem and engage in a relaxing occupation, a solution often springs to mind.

*"Knitting puts me in a quiet, contemplative, meditative
state of mind, and I often find if I am musing over
problematic issues while knitting, I will also
calmly work through solutions too."*

A simple yet powerful solution

Doing nothing or having nothing to do can be as stressful as having too much to do. Your brain needs occupation, purpose, structure and challenges to enable you to thrive, so the trick is getting the balance right. Your knitting can help you achieve balance in life.

When using Therapeutic Knitting as a tool for wellness I have noticed that men, in particular, like to knit for the process and may even undo their knitting to reuse the yarn. The process, and the ongoing reward of achieving regular moments of calm and enjoyment becomes their purpose and reward.

The insidious nature of modern-day stress can creep up on you unknowingly. Inevitable life events add to this stress burden. Setting aside twenty minutes to knit every day will encourage a habit of regular relaxation which will have far-reaching effects in all aspects of your life.

If you live a stressful life, it can be easy to forget what it feels like to be relaxed. Your brain adapts and learns that your stressed-out state is normal. The feeling you experience as your mind flows into the movements of knitting can teach you what it feels like to be truly relaxed again, and you can learn to recall this feeling even when you don't have your knitting to hand.

It's a good idea to plan in advance if you know you have an upcoming stressful event. Use your knitting to calm yourself beforehand and carry a portable kit to knit wherever and

Notes

Notes

whenever you need to. Have one handy in your bag to use for unforeseen circumstances and events too.

If you have perfectionist tendencies you need to be particularly aware of your levels of stress and anxiety.

A typical perfectionist will suffer stress every time they fail to reach their self-imposed perfectionist standards in every activity they do. Perfectionism can be a major source of stress and ill health.

As a child, I was taught it was desirable to set high standards, but there is a difference between setting high standards and unrealistic, unachievable ones. No-one is perfect and no-one ever reaches perfection in any task. We are all fallible human beings. I have learned through this work that striving for perfectionism is detrimental to my wellbeing and this realisation has enabled me to 'let go'. You can do it too.

I love the story of the Persian carpet makers who deliberately weave one mistake into their beautiful carpets. They do this because they believe only Allah is perfect.

One lady, a talented designer, who had been mulling over this story told me she had decided she needed to leave a mistake in her knitting. She followed this up with, *"but I can't quite decide where to leave it, because it needs to fit into the design".* If you are a perfectionist you will recognise her dilemma!

A simple yet powerful solution

Being successful necessitates a learning process which often involves trial and error.

We learn from making mistakes. They can lead you to amazing discoveries and breakthroughs – many of the world's finest inventions were made as a result of mistakes.

If you are a perfectionist, your prime focus should be on getting your mind into the flow of the knitting movements, rather than on the quality of your stitches. It is also important that you let 'mistakes' go, so for this purpose it is a good idea to have a 'free' knitting project on the go. A common statement I hear is *"You may not be able to see the mistake but I can."* It is a great example of how your brain focuses in on one aspect, and the more it focuses in, the more that particular thought grows, and the bigger the 'mistake' appears. More often than not, no-one else notices.

'Free knitting' is enjoyed purely for the process, where experimentation can take place and 'mistakes' are celebrated as unique quirks that make it special – an important part of the learning process. One of the traits of optimists is that when they experience setbacks they seek to learn lessons from the experience. Gradually you will learn to enjoy this freedom and realise that inconsistencies make the world a more interesting place.

Achieving a calm state of mind on a regular basis is highly beneficial to health and wellbeing in general and particularly

Notes

Notes

important if you suffer from ill health. Experiencing regular relaxation can turn down your stress system and tune up your healing system. Regularly entering a calm state of mind will strengthen those neural pathways so that relaxation becomes a habitual part of your life.

If you find yourself always busy, use your knitting to achieve a balance between active involvement and relaxing moments where your mind is at rest.

When your stress levels are high, healing is put on hold. Regular relaxation periods can enhance your body's natural healing process.

The feeling of loneliness is detrimental to health[14] but there is a huge difference between loneliness and solitude. It is possible to enjoy being alone and relish those moments of solitude and peace, and your knitting can help you achieve this. If you discover yourself feeling lonely, find yourself a knitting project to get engrossed in, learn a new skill, search the internet for new ideas, textures and colours, experiment, ask questions, think creatively. In doing this you will find you enjoy moments where you are completely engrossed in the enjoyment of the task – you will be 'in the flow'. Time will appear to pass differently.

Use the time you have alone to enjoy the peace and sanctuary of solitude.

A simple yet powerful solution

"When I'm lonely I knit and feel better."

Notes

If you find yourself on your own for the majority of time, actively seek out groups to join, visit the library to access their knitting and craft books, visit local markets to hunt out supplies, volunteer to teach someone to knit or help to run a knitting group. Join the Stitchlinks forum where you will find friends who care and understand.

The colour and texture of your yarn and needles will influence the way you feel too. If you're feeling low, use your knitting to raise your mood. You can maximise its benefits by choosing projects which are appropriate for you at that moment. The colours, textures and dialogues knitting brings into your home can enhance your environment. The creative process will enhance and broaden your thinking.

"It kept me engaged with pleasure, texture, colour and the belief that I was still an able person even though most bits of me didn't work well."

You will learn to look forward to and treasure those peaceful moments of solitude where your mind flows in harmony with your hands.

Quiet knitting will teach you the benefits of persistence, patience and planning – valuable skills in all areas of life.

Notes

Working on a project at home with a plan of showing it to your friends in a knitting group has many advantages. It gives you something to look forward to. Creating gifts for family and friends will encourage you to imagine, visualise and anticipate. Contributing to charity and knitting for people in need will nurture feelings of pride and self-worth. This can significantly change your outlook on life.

Most people immediately focus on the positive aspects of knitting in supportive groups when they first think of the benefits of knitting, but quiet knitting is just as important. It has different benefits. Combining the two will enable you to maximise the benefit to your health and wellbeing.

Use quiet knitting to improve your mood, manage stress, enhance your environment, change your thinking patterns and your outlook on life.

Discover and enjoy inner peace and learn to relish solitude without having to depend on others.

Use your knitting as a tool to enjoy both solitude and the company of others. You will find life will blossom and bloom from there.

A simple yet powerful solution

REVISIT YOUR GOALS

Now would be an appropriate time to revisit your goals. You may find they have changed. Take a moment to mull over what you have read and the notes you have made so far.

My Goals

1.

2.

3.

4.

5.

POINTS TO PERUSE

1. Set aside some time each day to knit. It will actively reduce your stress levels and encourage a habit of relaxation. It will have far-reaching effects in all aspects of your life.

2. Make getting your mind into the flow of the movements your prime focus if you are a perfectionist. Learn to let mistakes go with a piece of 'free knitting'. Celebrate them as a sign you have learned something new.

3. Learn to switch off for a period of time every day to give your mind a rest and your body time to heal. A daily dose of knitting will help you achieve this to improve your health and wellbeing.

4. Use your knitting to achieve a balance between an active involvement in life and restful moments of relaxation. Don't depend on others. The power is in your hands.

Notes

A simple yet powerful solution

5. Deliberately seek a state of relaxation every day. It won't happen by itself so use your knitting to achieve this and make it a habit.

6. Solve any problems you've been mulling over with a session of knitting. Research has shown that in a relaxed state, a solution often springs to mind.

7. Learn to enjoy and relish in moments of solitude, where your mind flows in harmony with your hands. Feeling happy in the peace of your own presence will help you manage feelings of loneliness and isolation.

8. Combine quiet knitting with knitting together in a group. The benefits of each are different. Used together they give you a powerful, portable tool at your fingertips.

Notes

My Notes

A simple yet powerful solution

-5-
KNITTING TOGETHER

Belong, laugh, enjoy – it's the fabric of life

· ·

The brilliant thing about knitting is...
it enables you to have fun and enjoy
the company of others even if you are
naturally shy or introverted...

Notes

Knitting creates and strengthens communities. Social knitting embraces the whole person within their community.

"There exists a bond of shared feeling that somehow goes beyond mere camaraderie."

Enjoying social contact is an important part of living life to the full. Social engagement has been found to be beneficial to health and wellbeing on many levels. A study in 2012 found that people who are socially engaged and mentally active are 40% less likely to develop dementia[15]. The combination of physical, mental and social activity is important.

Supportive friends can help you live a longer, healthier, happier life. Socially engaged people live longer because of the support and companionship they receive but also because of the help, information and knowledge they may obtain from others.

This effect isn't isolated to older adults, it applies across all age groups. Knitting groups provide a safe means of making friends across generations enabling you to develop a diverse supportive network. In the Stitchlinks / Cardiff University study[1], 90% of respondents said they had made several or more friends through knitting.

Another study has found that social engagement in rats resulted in a reduction in nerve pain[16]. The authors theorise that the stress of isolation increases levels of inflammation.

A simple yet powerful solution

"We believe socially paired individuals differ physiologically from socially isolated individuals and this difference is down to inflammation."[16]

The Stitchlinks / Cardiff University study[1] found that those who knitted together were more likely to feel calmer, happier, excited, useful and better about themselves. Knitting in a group had a significant impact on perceived happiness, learning new skills, improved social contact and communication with others. Those suffering from clinical depression benefited more in terms of feeling happier and better about themselves if they belonged to a knitting group than if they didn't.

"The therapy of collective knitting is priceless."

There is no doubt that enjoying supportive social contact is good for you and there are numerous benefits to belonging to a group even if you don't feel lonely. These include support from other members, mutual learning, sharing of information, having fun, and providing a support network which you can call on in times of need. Belonging is important. Knowing there is someone there in times of need is important. It gives you strength to live, to explore and enjoy life.

Even if you are an introvert preferring your own company, it still feels good to feel you belong somewhere. In the Stitchlinks / Cardiff University study[1], 86% of respondents told us that attending a knitting group gave them a feeling of belonging. It helps you build relationships of trust, opens

Notes

up an opportunity for conversation, enables you to tell and share your story and helps to reaffirm your place in society.

Social isolation is highly detrimental to health. Studies into the neuroscience of loneliness have shown that the feeling of loneliness sensitises your nervous system and affects your immune system. Loneliness can cause numerous health issues from heart attacks to depression and chronic pain. Neuroscientist John Cacioppo has found that the feeling of loneliness is as detrimental to health as smoking fifteen cigarettes a day[17].

In addition, if you feel lonely you can often find it harder to venture outside your own familiar surroundings, and as a result, your confidence and motivation will decline further so you become more isolated and less active, physically and mentally. If you think back to the Core Issues highlighted in Chapter 1, it's easy to feed into this cycle of loneliness, stress, low self-esteem and lack of rewarding occupation and develop secondary physical and mental health problems as a result.

Knitting groups local to you can help to build strong, supportive communities close to home.

Those with mental health issues or learning disabilities often feel they don't 'fit' into society and suffer a lifetime of isolation and consequent additional health problems. However, you don't have to be ill or live in an isolated area to feel

A simple yet powerful solution

lonely. Busy inner cities can feel like the loneliest of places, new mothers often feel isolated from the world as does anyone moving to a new area. It can be difficult to socialise for various reasons and it's easy to become socially isolated when you become unwell, or elderly.

Joining a group will not only help you to create and maintain a supportive network, it will also make you less prone to those secondary problems which can arise from feeling alone, such as overeating, an increasing sedentary lifestyle, mobility problems, low mood and lethargy.

*"Without it I would stay at home without
any connection to the outside world,
lacking in confidence and suffering
from anxiety and panic."*

It is important for humans to have the opportunity to 'just be' with others, without the need to feel they have to participate.

Many don't have this opportunity. Being together in the relaxed company of others is healing but it's normally only possible to experience this state with people you know well and feel comfortable with. The self-soothing activity of knitting makes it possible to feel comfortable with people you have never met before. You already have an interest in common, and if you don't feel like talking you can relax in the knowledge that it's perfectly acceptable to simply sit and knit quietly and 'just be'. It puts you in control.

Notes

*"The calm atmosphere that exists with a group of knitters
makes people feel comfortable and you don't
feel you have to talk either – you can just
sit in silence enjoying your knitting.*

"It opens you up to a different way of listening too."

✳   ✳   ✳

You will also find yourself laughing a lot. One of the noticeable things about knitting groups is the volume of laughter and easy banter that goes on. It's a relaxing, rejuvenating experience as the problems of the world are forgotten as you enjoy fun and time with friends. Enjoying, fun, laughter and relaxed conversation with friends in a safe environment is the opposite to your 'fight or flight' stress response[18] and will enable your body's natural healing system to kick in.

Social laughter is also correlated with an elevated pain threshold[19]. So those who experience pain can benefit in a number of ways from belonging to a knitting group.

✳   ✳   ✳

Attending a new group for the first few times can, however, be quite daunting. It's not easy joining a group even for the more confident among us. For those with low self-confidence or the naturally introverted it can be too stressful, so you can easily become more isolated. Your knitting will enable you to take that first step and you will soon begin to enjoy the company of others.

Notes

There appears to be a synergistic relationship between knitting and the group. The activity of knitting provides a self-soothing tool to manage feelings of anxiety or fear at attending a group for the first time or at times when you may be feeling vulnerable. The knitting group, on the other hand, enhances the benefits of knitting as an individual activity.

"Going to parties or other social gatherings is terrifying to me. Imagine my surprise at signing up and driving to a class on how to knit a Shetland shawl without any panic or worry. I was looking forward to it. Knitting gave me the courage to reach out and socialise with other knitters. I'm actively looking for knitting clubs, groups, and events to go to. Not just to learn new things, but to interact with other people. That's pretty amazing for me."

Returning to the point made in Chapter 2, the position of your hands as you knit contributes to the feeling of safety and comfort in situations where you may otherwise feel anxious or threatened. This further enhances the feeling of relaxation.

The fact that you can choose to engage in eye contact with others...or not, means you are in control.

Therapeutic Knitting groups are safe places. They provide a secure environment to meet others from a variety of different backgrounds. The common activity provides a reason to

Notes

attend and an easy point of conversation so you won't need to worry about what to talk about or whether you'll have anything in common with others in your group. The conversation will flow naturally – initially about colours and textures and knitting techniques, but it easily drifts to other areas of life. This can cover a variety of comments and topics which will provide you with information and opinions from a wide range of individuals you may otherwise not have access to or contact with.

Groups also provide an opportunity to 'tell your story' in a safe community. Voicing your story out loud can help to change your perspective on the world. It will help to establish norms and thereby put problems into perspective. You will learn that you are not alone in the world.

> *"I would argue that community is built once*
> *the needles are taken out of your bag.*
> *A space for conversation opens up."*

For those who are ill or embroiled in personal problems, the knitting activity will provide an alternative, positive focus of conversation away from problems. It gives you something else to talk about – an alterKNITive focus of attention.

People from all different walks of life, different cultures, educational backgrounds and ethnic groups can come together to knit and find a common thread in a complex world. Firm friendships are formed between people who

A simple yet powerful solution

might otherwise have never met. Life roles can be reversed in the knitting group – someone who left school at sixteen can become a skilled teacher to a university professor and that has benefits for all concerned. Knitting in a group levels the playing field. It can result in you 'seeing', 'listening' and 'communicating' with people differently. It's an overwhelmingly accepting environment and can enable people from minority groups to integrate into a community.

In many modern societies, the important element of 'touch' is missing from people's lives. It has almost become unacceptable to touch your fellow human unless you know them well. Supportive, reassuring touch can convey so much more than words. Knitting together can encourage people to interact in this way in a safe environment.

In the workplace, lunchtime knitting groups can be a means of managing stress and enhancing communication – a place where those lower down the chain can sit equally in the company of managers. Getting to know each other on an informal basis in the 'company knitting group' can be a great way of building a strong working team. Likewise, if there is someone who is having problems 'fitting in' with the team, the workplace knitting group can be a good place to bring individuals together in a relaxed, safe setting.

Used in a healthcare environment, groups can help build social confidence but also to provide a source of information,

Notes

Notes

advice, education, monitoring, motivation and support over the longer term. They can also be used to impart health information to ethnic minority groups or abused women who may otherwise not have access to supportive groups because of religious, cultural or enforced social restrictions.

Knitting groups with a clinical focus can become group therapy sessions for people with mental health issues or those with addictions such as drug, alcohol and smoking. Shifting the focus away from the problem whilst encouraging people to talk in a safe environment can work well.

These are what I call non-medical, medical groups and I think this is an interesting, exciting way of supporting the self-management of health and wellness as well as long-term medical conditions.

The Stitchlinks / Cardiff University study[1] showed that those who attended a group (virtual or face-to-face) were more likely to feel that knitting had enabled them to learn new knitting skills plus a wide range of transferable, practical skills such as IT skills, patience, planning as well as social and communication skills and strategies for coping with life.

Once settled in a knitting group, you will soon find yourself observing new skills and wanting to learn more. They are a great place for learning, either together or from each other. It is important to keep learning throughout life – it keeps your brain healthy. It nurtures creative thought and ability and a desire to learn new knitting skills as well as other related skills such as using a computer to search for patterns and materials.

A regular dose of novelty is important for building new brain cells and neural pathways and you'll have no problem keeping your creative thoughts flowing if you attend a knitting group on a regular basis.

If you don't have a knitting group in your area, why not think about starting one? The Groups page of the Stitchlinks website has all the information you need to get started. As I have discovered, on a personal level it is highly rewarding and fun.

Supportive social contact is important for wellbeing. Social isolation and loneliness are harmful to health in many ways.

Regularly attending a knitting group can help you to grow and develop many life skills which are crucial for wellbeing. It can also enable you to develop a supportive social network and nurture that very basic human need to belong. Looking back at Maslow's Hierarchy (Chapter 1), it will move you up that ladder of human needs, closer to your personal pinnacle.

The self-soothing activity of knitting combined with the hand position takes away many of the fears of social situations and attending a group.

Notes

Knitting enables socialisation and participation, and from there your confidence will bloom.

As you have seen, knitting alone and knitting together have a number of different benefits. Becoming involved in both is a winning combination.

Belong, laugh, enjoy and make it the fabric of your life...

A simple yet powerful solution

REFLECT FOR A MOMENT

The next few Chapters focus on 'the doing', so take a moment to reflect on what you would like to achieve from knitting alone and knitting within a group. Revisit and refine your goals if necessary. Research knitting groups in your area.

Groups Near Me

1.

2.

3.

4.

5.

POINTS TO PERUSE

1. Join a local knitting group to enhance the benefits of knitting, discover new friends and build a strong support network.

2. Use the self-soothing movements and hand position of knitting to ease any stress or anxiety you may feel at attending a group. Remember, you already have lots in common.

3. Encourage your body's natural healing system by having fun with supportive friends. Laughter and easy banter with friends is the opposite of your stress 'fight or flight' response[18].

4. Enjoy participating in conversation on a range of topics. It will open your mind, expand your world, teach you new things and enable you to 'tell your story' in a safe community.

Notes

5. Enjoy 'just being' in the company of others. Sit and knit quietly whilst enjoying the 'presence' of the group around you.

6. Learn to 'see', 'listen' and 'communicate' differently with people from a range of backgrounds. It will enable you to view the world from a different perspective.

7. Start up or attend a lunchtime, work-based knitting group. It will help you manage stress levels and introduce you to new people whilst building a team spirit.

8. Learn new knitting skills from, or alongside, others in the group. Use the group and the expertise of others to stimulate your creative juices, whilst sharing your knowledge too.

Notes

My Notes

A simple yet powerful solution

-6-
SIT
WELL

Improve your knitting posture

• •

The brilliant thing about knitting is...

you can do it anywhere.

Most of us do it sitting...

Notes

Getting into the habit of sitting well and moving regularly will ensure you maximise your wellness and increase your enjoyment of knitting. And, as an added bonus, you will look good too.

It is possible to knit standing up, sitting in a chair, on a bus, in a wheelchair or in bed. Some even do it walking and running.

Most of us knit sitting down, so to maximise its therapeutic benefits you should know how to sit comfortably, but well. Moreover, it is crucial to develop a habit of changing your position and moving regularly. This chapter is about doing just that.

Those of us who are fit and healthy may get away with slouching on the sofa for the time being, but remember that repeated actions become habits, mentally and physically. Good posture is a result of good habit, bad posture is a result of bad habits accumulated over the years and the longer you indulge, the harder these patterns of behaviour will be to break.

It therefore makes sense to get into good habits early. Not only will it help you to avoid or minimise back, neck and hand pain later in life, it will soon become a natural part of living life positively and well.

Posture describes the way you hold your body against gravity. Maintaining good posture means training yourself to become

A simple yet powerful solution

aware of how you hold yourself in all activities, not in a rigid way but in a relaxed, intuitive one. As with all things, this will become automatic as your brain becomes practised at the feeling. Poor posture will have become a habit for most of us, particularly as we age, so it will feel strange at first to sit well. Don't worry, your brain just needs to adapt to the sensation of the new position and then it will begin to feel 'normal'.

Many of the aches and pains we experience are triggered by poor posture. It can even affect the functioning of internal organs by restricting the space your lungs and other vital organs have to work in, making you feel unwell and tired.

Those who enjoy good posture stand out from the crowd. They look poised, in control and healthy. Adopting a good posture will not only help your body function more efficiently, it will also make you feel better about yourself, improve your confidence and can even make you look slimmer.

As you move through life, many factors contribute to the way you hold your body. These can be physical, such as injury, muscle tension, tiredness and pain or just plain bad habit. Your mental state also plays an important part. Think back to those Core Issues in Chapter 1 because they can affect posture too. Stress, for example, can cause you to tense up, as can anxiety, whilst depression or low self-esteem can cause you to slouch and lose interest in the way you look. All these factors can result in an alteration in the normal alignment of your body, particularly your spine and the

Notes

position of your head on your neck. This will eventually lead to pain and stiffness.

Achieving a good posture not only makes you look good, but it can also prevent or decrease those aches and pains. So it's important to increase your awareness and actively consider your posture on an ongoing basis. Sitting for long periods can cause stiffness, particularly in your spine, hips, knees and ankles. Certain muscles, ligaments and nerves can become tight and short in these areas. If you have a tendency to slouch, this can restrict your breathing and put pressure on vital organs.

The good news is that it is in your power to change poor posture. Be mindful of the way you sit as you knit and adopt a habit of changing position and moving regularly.

If you have a particular health condition and need more help, a chartered physiotherapist will be able to give you exercises and stretches with your specific needs in mind.

Improving your posture will need perseverance because it is bound to feel strange at first. It will all be worth it though, as you will be rewarded with long-term physical benefits plus it will help you to feel really good about yourself.

Choosing the right chair for your individual needs is a crucial factor in achieving good sitting posture while you knit. Try

A simple yet powerful solution

not to knit sitting on a low sofa as this will encourage you to slouch over your work. In addition, your knees will be higher than your hips, making it difficult to maintain a good posture and potentially making it a struggle to stand from this position. Sitting like this every day will store up problems for the future. Many knitters also use their computers to search for patterns and materials so the same approach applies to sitting at your computer too. If you use a laptop, take care not to slouch over it.

Choose a chair which –

- Enables your feet to rest flat on the floor
- Enables your hips to rest slightly higher than your knees
- Supports the natural curves of your back
- Has a firm seat which is long enough to support your whole thigh, but no longer.

Some points to bear in mind –

- Sit with the base of your spine against the back of the chair
- Balance your weight evenly on your sitting bones
- Place both feet flat on the floor
- Try placing a small, rolled up towel in the curve of your lower back to support this area
- Gently roll your shoulders back – don't round them over your work
- Relax your arms, shoulders and jaw
- Be aware of your neck posture

Notes

- Be aware of the position of your head on your neck –
  a poking chin will put strain on your neck
- Use a good light
- Take breaks to do some gentle finger and wrist stretches
- Take regular breaks to walk around and stretch to stimulate
  your circulation
- Take regular breaks to focus on a distant object to avoid
  potential eye strain
- Pace your knitting – don't knit until it hurts. It's better to
  rest and do some more later.

Even if you adopt a good posture, sitting for long periods
can make you feel tired as a result of poor circulation and
decreased oxygen getting to your vital organs. Prolonged
inactivity can be a factor in the formation of blood clots in
the legs (DVTs) in the same way as when you take a long
plane journey. So, to minimise the risks of sitting, take regular
breaks about every twenty minutes to gently stretch your
joints, including your hands. If you are able to take a walk
around the garden or house, this will help to ease tension in
muscles and boost your circulation, sending more oxygen to
your brain to make you more alert. Take the opportunity to
focus on a distant object to avoid eye strain, too.

If, by the nature of your work or health condition, you have
to spend a lot of time sitting, it is important to ensure you
get up and move around regularly to get your circulation
and oxygen flowing – treat it as thinking time. Similarly if
you spend a lot of time online visiting knitting forums or

A simple yet powerful solution

searching for patterns and materials, play close attention to the way you sit and the amount of time you spend in this position. If you are unable to stand or walk, it's even more important to spend time regularly stretching and moving as far as you are able.

Research has shown that sitting for long periods is detrimental to health[20]. As knitting is a sedentary activity you should pay attention to the overall time you spend sitting each day. This might require changing your daily habits. If you are able, plan to stand for tasks you would normally sit for. Many people now stand at their computers using desks specifically for this purpose. Cooking can also be done while standing, so take some time to look at the overall picture for your average day because everything you do counts.

Over many years of helping people to knit therapeutically I have developed ways of adapting this basic sitting posture and the knitting technique to suit individual problems and requirements. The most common I encounter is painful hands, upper limbs or necks. Many people with arthritis of the hands, wrists or neck, or conditions such as fibromyalgia affecting the hands and arms, stop activities such as knitting for fear it will cause harm. They may have been life-long knitters who really loved and miss the activity. Others who have painful hands may be new to knitting and wish to use it as therapy or a hobby but feel reluctant to give it a go for fear of making their pain worse.

Notes

The good news is that movement is good for you providing it is paced properly.

If you suffer from hand pain, check with your doctor before you start and rest during any flare up. Any enforced 'down time' doesn't need to be unproductive, though. Use it to plan, anticipate and look forward to future projects. Staying involved in this way will help you to remain positive.

Knitting is a great hand exercise and there are very few medical conditions where a doctor would advise you not to move. Movement and exercise are good for you. Inactivity will lead to muscle and ligament weakness, stiff joints and ultimately more pain. A phrase often used by clinicians is 'motion is lotion'.

"Knitting has been very helpful, my hands were so sore from arthritis that I couldn't hold needles for long, but now I can and my hands are more supple."

The good news is that not only can you continue to knit despite hand problems, you can use your knitting as a tool to improve them.

This might entail changing your knitting habits a little, but this is all part of adapting and changing with the flow of life. I have successfully enabled patients with a range of hand problems to discover or rediscover the benefits and joy of Therapeutic Knitting.

A simple yet powerful solution

If your hands and wrists have a tendency to ache during or after a spell of knitting, you may need to pace your activity and incorporate more rest and stretching periods. These precautions can go a long way to preventing injuries such as repetitive strain (RSI) which could stop you knitting altogether, so get into some good practice right from the start.

You may need to adapt the basic sitting posture outlined at the beginning of this chapter if you suffer from neck, arm, wrist or hand pain. I have experimented with knitting aids and my patients and I always come back to these useful posture adaptations –

- Place a pillow across your lap to support the weight of your hands and forearms
- Relax your shoulders and jaw – gently ease your shoulder blades down and back
- Be aware of your neck and 'head on neck' posture. Gently tuck your chin in
- Use circular needles to take the weight of your project off your hands and neck
- Keep your elbows tucked into your side along your body so that you knit with 'short arms'
- Avoid looking down for prolonged periods by raising your hands up on a pillow and clipping your pattern to a copy board (the type secretaries use)
- Take regular breaks to stretch your hands and fingers – the frequency will entirely depend on your condition but

Notes

Notes

everyone should take a break every 20-30 minutes
• Be particularly vigilant about pacing your knitting – knit
  in small chunks of time to avoid an increase in pain.

You will need a bed pillow and be prepared to experiment a little. If you suffer from a lot of pain it is a good idea to do this with a friend who can pass a selection of pillows to you to try out. Place the pillow across your lap so your hands are resting gently in a position which will enable them to lie with your elbows at about ninety degrees and your shoulders gently relaxed – take care that the pillow doesn't push your shoulders towards your ears. The firmness of the pillow should enable it to absorb the full weight of your hands but enable you to knit with a fluid motion. In this position your neck, arms and hands can relax fully.

The pillow absorbs the weight of your arms, needles and knitting project so that all that is required are the rhythmic movements of your hands. You will learn to adapt the degree of movement you are comfortable with, and the length of time you are comfortable knitting for, and gradually build on this as your hands become accustomed to the movements.

"I have made small changes to the way I sit when I knit and it's made a big difference. I can enjoy knitting comfortably again, providing I don't knit for too long."

During this process you will learn the difference between the ache of unaccustomed exercise and the pain of having done

A simple yet powerful solution

too much. We all ache after performing an unfamiliar exercise but the discomfort will ease off after a couple of days, so don't be afraid if your hands ache a bit when you start knitting again. If it doesn't ease after a day or two, plan on doing a little less knitting in your next sitting when the pain has subsided and gradually build from there. It's all about finding your baseline of activity from which you can build. More on this in Chapter 9.

You can minimise the risk of developing pain in your hands or repetitive strain injury if you adopt a good sitting posture and pace your knitting.

If you already have hand, arm or neck pain you can continue to knit by making small changes to your sitting posture, knitting technique and by paying close attention to pacing your activity.

Good posture is the result of good habit and it makes sense to start getting into good habits early.

Get into the routine of sitting well and you will reap the benefits well into the future.

POINTS TO PERUSE

1. Get into the habit of taking regular breaks to move, walk around and stretch your legs and hands. It will keep your circulation flowing and minimise the risks of sitting for too long.

2. Take time to look out of the window and focus on a distant object on a regular basis – about every twenty minutes. This will help to prevent eye strain.

3. Improve your confidence and even look slimmer by practising good posture and making it a habit. Be mindful of your posture.

4. Be aware that other issues affect posture. Low mood, muscle tension or stress can encourage you to slouch, so pay particular attention to your posture if you are prone to these conditions.

Notes

A simple yet powerful solution

5. Choose a suitable chair for your body size and shape for maximum comfort and health benefits.

6. Pay attention to the overall time you spend sitting in a full day. Sitting for long periods is detrimental to health. It may mean changing the way you do some activities.

7. Adapt your posture and knitting materials if you suffer from hand, arm or neck pain. It will mean you can continue to knit and enjoy the activity.

8. Think about your posture while using your computer too, particularly if you have a habit of hunching over a laptop. Sit well while searching for patterns and information.

Notes

My Notes

A simple yet powerful solution

-7-
PREPARE FOR ACTION

Choose the yarn and needles for you

• •

The brilliant thing about knitting is... even planning and preparing your projects is beneficial and exciting...

Notes

To maximise the therapeutic benefits of knitting you should consider your choice of materials.

The materials you use will contribute significantly to your pleasure. When planning your project consider the type of needles plus the thickness, colour and texture of your yarn. You will also learn to use different types of project for different benefits and I talk about this in more detail in the next chapter.

A primary consideration of Therapeutic Knitting is the ability to 'get your mind into the flow of the movements' and I cover this in greater detail in Chapter 9. Your choice of materials can influence this, so you will find it beneficial to consider this requirement when planning your projects. In general, I have found the average, optimum needle size to be around 4mm. It is considerably more difficult to achieve a good flow of movement with large or heavy needles.

Choosing a project which requires double knitting yarn and 4mm needles is a good place to start.

*　　*　　*

So let's take a look at needles...

Personal preference will play the biggest part in your choice of needles – opt for those which give you the most pleasure to knit with. It's worth experimenting with a range of needles to find the best for you. If you belong to a knitting group, ask to try out different types or get together as a group to buy a selection of needles for people to experiment with.

These days, knitting needles are available in a range of materials but it often comes down to the wooden or metal debate. Many people with hand problems prefer to use wooden needles because they have slightly more give and are warmer, but don't assume that this will be the case for you – experiment with wooden, plastic and metal to discover your personal preference. Each material has its pros and cons. In general, I have found those with hand problems prefer to knit with polished birch needles.

Stitches tend to slide less easily on wooden needles, so some of you may find that this adds 'resistance' to the flow of your movements. If this is the case you may prefer the more slippery metal ones. Polished birch provides a happy medium whilst retaining the warmer, more flexible properties of wood. They also tend to have sharper points than the bamboo variety which can be a bit too blunt to enable continuity of movement. Some of you, on the other hand, may prefer the less slippery nature of bamboo needles because they enable you to control your stitches, particularly if you're prone to 'losing' them off the ends of metal ones.

There are knitters who love the slipperiness and sharpness of metal needles and the flow it gives their knitting plus, of course, there's that rhythmic, meditative click which you don't get with wooden ones. Some, on the other hand, find the click

Notes

annoying. If you enjoy knitting in front of the TV with your family or in bed at night, the rhythmic click of metal needles may not be as meditative and calming for those around you. So the message is, experiment and don't discount plastic – they've come a long way in recent years. They are usually lighter and their multitude of colours can be a lot of fun!

In general, the more you spend on needles, the better the quality. Beware the cheaper wooden ones as they tend to be a little rough and blunt – the added friction will interfere with the flow of your movements. Once you've identified your material of choice, buying one good pair of 4mm needles to get you started is a great investment in your future wellbeing. They will see you through many projects and happy hours of knitting. Don't forget that wooden needles can snap if you stand or sit on them, so get into the habit of storing your knitting safely when not in use.

Having chosen your needle material, the next debate is straight, circular or even square circulars! Modern, good quality circular needles are brilliant. They come in a range of interchangeable sizes, materials and uplifting colours. It's worth investing a little as the more expensive types have highly flexible inter-connecting cables so you're not constantly wrestling with a rigid tangle of plastic and yarn. You may like to consider buying a set with a range of interchangeable points and cable lengths if you decide that circular needles are the way to go.

A simple yet powerful solution

In terms of the therapeutic aspect, circular needles are particularly good if you have painful hands, arms or neck because the weight of your knitting can rest in your lap and you only have short ends to hold which greatly reduces the strain. Don't worry – you don't have to start knitting everything 'in the round' as they can be used exactly like straight needles.

If you have hand, arm or neck pain, I would recommend giving circular needles a go, plus the pillow support as discussed in the previous chapter.

You can also buy square-shaped needles and, as the name suggests, they are square in cross section as opposed to round in diameter. The theory is that square-shaped needles are more comfortable to grip for those with hand problems and produce a more even stitch. None of my patients have liked them enough to invest in a pair but I do know knitters who find them helpful and love them. Again it is down to personal taste and, above all, comfort. And yes, they are available as straight needles and square circulars.

Getting your posture and choice of needles right is all about personal comfort and enhancing your enjoyment of the process to gain maximal therapeutic benefit from the flow of the movements. Take some time to experiment a little.

Those with hand pain often fall into the trap of choosing projects with thicker needles in the belief that they will be

Notes

Notes

easier to hold – indeed this may be the case when you are grasping empty needles. Take into account that they will be heavier, need thicker yarn and ultimately result in a heavier project. It's also much more difficult to get into the flow of movement with bigger needles – and that's what we're trying to achieve. At the other end of the scale, very thin needles can be difficult to hold and the fine grip can be tiring. 4mm, 4.5mm and 5mm are a good size to start with if you're prone to hand problems.

If you are stressed you will find your stress is often reflected in your knitting and your stitches will be tighter as a result. If you're particularly stressed and find your knitting tension matches your personal tension, I would encourage you to use 4.5mm needles with double knitting yarn and concentrate on working with looser stitches. In fact, you can use the tension of your knitting as excellent feedback for how stressed you actually are.

If you love sock or lace knitting with fine yarns, intersperse these projects with ones which use thicker needles to give your hands a break from the fine grip needed for these.

Your choice of yarn is also important. In the Stitchlinks / Cardiff University study[1], knitters told us that the texture of the yarn was significantly more important than colour for influencing their mood. 24% of respondents told us colour was important whereas 49% said texture was. Work I do with

A simple yet powerful solution

patients supports this finding – touching something good makes you feel good.

The tactile experience translates into an emotional response.

It may be that touching something soft stirs deep memories of snuggling up to our mothers when we were babies. Children learn to associate soft things with positive feelings, and those memories can be evoked in adulthood.

> *"I get great pleasure from the colours*
> *and feel of the yarn."*

A well-known experiment by psychologist Harry Harlow in the 1950s found that baby monkeys separated from their mothers shortly after birth chose to cling to a wire frame covered with soft terry cloth even when their food came from bottles attached to bare, wire-framed surrogate mothers[21].

Many of the narratives I receive talk about the pleasure knitters get from stroking beautiful yarn. The quote below always makes me smile –

> *"On days when I'm not able to do much*
> *I stroke my stash and it makes me feel good."*

As you are stroking your stash, you are planning, anticipating and looking forward, which is positive input even on days when you may be feeling under the weather.

Notes

For your Therapeutic Knitting projects, opt for soft yarn which has a little 'give' but no 'bits', particularly if you have a tendency towards achy hands. The good news is that it doesn't necessarily mean expensive. There are perfectly acceptable acrylic yarns out there enabling you to be prolific without breaking the bank. If you can get along to your local yarn store it's a good idea to carry out a 'softness / give' test before you buy. Yarn without any 'give' can be hard on painful fingers, hands and wrists. Extra bits, furry stuff and fluff can get caught up in the stitches which will add to the stress on your hands and affect the flow of your movements.

Be wary of cotton if you have hand problems – it can feel beautifully soft but, in general, it has little to no 'give' so can be hard on your hands. If, like me, you like soft cotton, it's a good idea to limit your time knitting with it, stopping before your hands begin to object.

Of course the thickness and type of yarn you choose is dependent on your pattern, so while planning your projects this is something to bear in mind. Thicker yarn may seem easier to hold initially, but you need to take into account that it requires bigger, heavier needles and, as your knitting grows, so will the weight of your project. Double Knitting (DK) is a good place to start.

This doesn't mean, however, that you should never knit with thick, fine or fluffy yarns. Variety is good and it will expand your creative mind to explore different projects and tactile

Notes

experiences. Simply be aware to pace your time with unusual yarns and intersperse these projects with ones that are kinder to your hands and enable a freer flow of movement. Plan your projects and swap them around for maximum benefit. More on that in the next chapter.

I am often asked whether it's possible to enhance the knitting experience and I would suggest this is down to individual preference. Some find that listening to music enhances the meditative-like state. Others enjoy knitting outside in gardens and parks – being outside in nature is beneficial to health so will add to your experience.

Perhaps the stereotypical granny got it right – adding in the rhythmic movement of a rocking chair may be the ultimate enhancement to Therapeutic Knitting.

Research on the merits of rocking in rocking chairs for health lists benefits ranging from decreased anxiety and pain to improved mood, relaxation, better balance[22] and even quicker post-operative recovery and healing. Combining the rhythm of rocking with the rhythm of knitting may be the way to go.

Planning and preparing your projects will inspire you and engage your brain in visualisation, imagination, forward-thinking thought processes and anticipation, which will all benefit your brain health and wellbeing.

Notes

"Being inspired boosts your confidence."

Your choice of materials will contribute significantly to your knitting experience.

Now you have chosen the yarn and needles to maximise the benefits to you, it's time to consider a range of projects...

A simple yet powerful solution

My Favourite Yarns and Colours

In preparation for the next chapter, which looks at different projects and their aims, take some time to reflect on your favourite yarns and colours and list them below.

POINTS TO PERUSE

1. Practise getting your mind into the flow of the movements. Let your mind and hands flow in harmony and get it down to a fine art. Your choice of materials will affect the flow of movement.

2. Start with a project which requires double knitting (DK) yarn and 4mm needles. It's the best way to practise getting into the flow.

3. Try out different types and materials of needle, but be aware of cheap wooden needles. In general, the more expensive needles are smoother and more luxurious to touch.

4. Give circular needles a go if you suffer from hand, arm or neck pain. They enable the weight of your project to rest on your lap or cushion. Square needles are worth a try too.

Notes

5. Choose the texture of your yarn carefully. Give it a softness test before buying. Remember, the tactile experience will translate into an emotional response.

6. Be aware of cotton or yarn with bits or fluff – it can be hard on your hands. If you love to knit with it, intersperse these projects with those that are kinder to your hands.

7. Ensure you swap your projects around and gently stretch your hands regularly if you like knitting socks or lace. Give your hands regular rest periods.

8. Stroke your stash, plan and prepare your projects to encourage your mind to look forward, anticipate and raise mood on days when you can't, for whatever reason, knit.

Notes

My Notes

A simple yet powerful solution

-8-
PLAN YOUR PROJECTS

Enjoy projects with specific aims in mind

· ·

The brilliant thing about knitting is... there are numerous projects to choose from and always something to learn whatever your skill level...

Notes

Choosing a range of projects can maximise the benefits and help you to address specific issues.

If you are using knitting therapeutically, it is a good idea to have a few different projects on the go and swapping them around according to how you feel and your mood of the moment. It is a personal choice as to what type of project you would like to include in your Therapeutic Knitting tool kit, so a good place to start is to make a list of what you would like your knitting to help you achieve.

Some common aims are to facilitate relaxation, experience calm, improve sleep patterns, manage stress, use distraction, enjoy social contact, make using public transport easier and create gifts for friends, family and charity.

I have found it helpful to choose projects from the following ideas – an 'intricate' project, a 'novelty' project, an 'automatic' project, a 'group' project, a 'big' project, a 'quick-fix' project, a 'bag' project and a 'free knitting' project. Each can fulfil a specific purpose and your choice will vary according to your skill level and what you would like to achieve.

An 'intricate' project, or one that requires your full attention, can help to distract your mind from any problems or pain you might have. The level will very much depend on your knitting skills. When I was teaching myself the basics of lace knitting I had an easy lace shawl on the go as that was

A simple yet powerful solution

complex enough for me at the time. You may like to combine an 'intricate' project with your 'novelty' project – one that teaches you new skills. There are always new techniques to learn and skills to master, so it is important to keep challenging yourself to something different.

Brain studies have shown that regularly introducing new skills or approaches is important for brain health[23]. Regular novelty, good diet and cardiovascular exercise are the cornerstones of neuroplasticity – that's your nervous system's (including your brain) ability to change with experience[24]. The more you can do to facilitate this process of plasticity in a positive way, the better your chances of maximising your wellness. Making the introduction of new skills and regular novelty an ongoing process in your life will enhance it in many ways.

> *"The intricacy of the project depends on the mood. Happy mood doesn't require much more than a little stockinette, while anger and sadness might need a more complicated pattern to take my mind off things."*

Use an 'intricate' project to distract your mind from problems and a 'novelty' project to stimulate learning and the growth of new brain pathways.

In contrast to your 'intricate' project, have an 'automatic' one on the go too. This will enable you to knit without thinking about the process or the pattern. It will enable your mind to roam without limit – where your mind knows no boundaries.

Notes

A state where it can dream, plan, enjoy being unrealistic, or just 'be' in a space which extends to infinity. It's a wonderful place to visit and one which gives your mind a break from the hassles of everyday life. One knitter described this mind-state as –

"Having the power to give your mind a mini-break whenever you need to."

An 'automatic' project is also great for when you're in the company of others so your hands can move automatically whilst you engage in conversation. Many knitters have a specific 'group' project for this purpose – one which will enable them to knit, chat, have eye contact… or not, and enjoy fun and laughter with others all at the same time. Taking an 'intricate' project to a group invariably leads to mistakes, so plan in advance. Of course what is complicated to one knitter is easy for another, so take a little time to think through your requirements.

Use your 'automatic' project to give your mind a mini break from life's problems. A 'group' project will enable you to enjoy the laughter and easy banter of your knitting friends.

A 'big' project is next on my list. I have knitted a range of colourful, tactile throws and love having one ongoing in the background – it's like a reliable friend, always there to comfort me. It even keeps me warm as I'm knitting. And, of course, when it comes to throws it's really up to you when you

A simple yet powerful solution

choose to cast off and move on to something new. A 'big' project will enable you to enjoy the journey plus give you a huge sense of achievement when you decide that journey should end. Don't put a time limit on when you want it completed as this will put you under unnecessary pressure.

In contrast, it's a good idea to have a 'quick-fix' project at hand – one that gives fast results for those days when you need a boost in mood. Fingerless mittens, hats, socks or clothing for premature babies are good examples of a 'quick-fix'. Choose a level of complexity which requires a little effort but ensures success. You will enhance your mood even more by knitting your 'quick-fix' project in a luxuriously tactile yarn in your favourite colour. You can further enhance the feel-good effect by giving your knitted item as a gift to a friend or to charity. As you are knitting think about how good it feels to be giving to others.

If you're feeling down, a 'quick-fix' project in a vibrant colour and soft texture is the way to go.

Producing an end product results in wonderful feelings of achievement which will flush your brain with a boost of feel-good chemicals. This great feeling of accomplishment can be motivating. If your self-esteem or mood is low, a finished knitted item will enable you to contribute through gift giving and charity donations – so you can achieve a feeling of wellbeing in a number of ways. To pick up the point I made in Chapter 3, research has shown that giving to charity

Notes

stimulates the release of feel-good chemicals in your brain[12], so if you're feeling down, knitting for charity will help you whilst helping someone else too. It's a win, win situation.

> *"It brings me an enormous boost in self-esteem,*
> *making beautiful garments, bags*
> *and shawls that people praise."*

If you have a tendency to suffer from anxiety, panic, pain spasms, or low social confidence when out and about, it can help to organise a 'bag' project which is stored in your bag at all times. The rhythm of your movements will be immediately calming and familiar, and the distraction will help to focus your brain's attention away from panicky feelings. It will help you to feel in control and this can significantly change your outlook on life and encourage you to go out. More on this in Chapter 10.

> *"Knitting is something I can do anywhere with very*
> *little tools. I take my knitting on the train*
> *and other situations where I am*
> *prone to be more anxious."*

'Bag' projects can also be used to manage stress or relieve boredom on the commute to work, whilst waiting for hospital appointments or on long journeys. They are also good for carers. Writer Merlin Mann describes knitting as a good interstitial activity – one that can fill otherwise unproductive time. It can also be picked up and dropped at any time.

A simple yet powerful solution

"Knitting fulfils the three criteria of a good interstitial-time activity: it's portable, it can be done amid distractions, and even a few seconds spent on it contributes to the end result."
Merlin Mann.

Notes

Use a 'quick-fix' project for fast reward and a small 'bag' project to manage anxiety, panic, stress or boredom when out and about.

A 'free knitting' project is a one where you cast on and knit without a pattern, going where your creative mind takes you. 'Free knitting' is great for encouraging you to experiment with different stitch patterns, or simply playing and having fun with the yarn to stimulate your creativity.

If you are a perfectionist or feel your creative self needs a helping hand then I would recommend having a 'free knitting' project on the go. Ignore any mistakes and enjoy it simply for the pleasure of the process and fun of experimentation.

People I teach to knit often begin their knitting experience creating squares of different sizes and textures. Squares and rectangles provide a simple structure whilst still promising the potential to become something useful. They are also a great way of learning new stitch combinations – a cushion cover or blanket created from squares of different stitch combinations, yarns, colours and textures makes an easy end

Notes

product achievable by all. However, within that 'easy' structure the knitter can experiment with more complex creative combinations of stitch patterns if they so desire.

A 'square' project can also become a team project – members of the group can knit squares which can be sewn together in a team effort. Group members can help new knitters to sew or crochet their squares together and this team focus helps to build confidence and create friendships as individuals help each other.

A wonderful example of this was I Knit[13] and Water Aid's 'Knit a River' campaign which invited knitters around the world to knit a blue 15cm x 15cm square. They received donations of nearly 100,000 squares from all over the globe. When sewn together the final 'river' of blue knitted squares measured approximately 2,000ft and was carried by 200 knitters through London to Downing Street as a knitted petition to draw attention to water poverty. Of course your team project doesn't have to be on such a huge scale – squared blankets can be knitted for your local care home or animal sanctuary.

Larger, individual squares knitted in soft cotton can be used as dishcloths or face cloths. Dishcloth knitting is a big craze in the US. It's one I didn't understand at first, but when I knitted my first bright yellow face cloth in gorgeous soft cotton with a heart-shaped indent I was hooked. They make wonderful soft cloths and add colour and individuality to your home.

They also make great window and glass cleaners, so now I have them around the house. They make a great portable, 'group' or 'quick-fix' project too. However, as I mentioned previously, if you have a tendency for achy hands, choose cotton yarn carefully and limit the time you spend knitting with it in one session.

'Square' projects can be as easy or complex as you desire and are a great way of developing your free creative mind.

Other projects you might like to consider are team projects and knitalongs. They can motivate you to get involved in a charity project or you may wish to learn a new skill such as lace knitting together with friends. Team activities can take place in your face-to-face group or via the internet where you can post pictures and share ideas with knitters around the world. They can build local and global communities.

Colour and texture can enhance your knitting experience so use this to your advantage, particularly if you're feeling a bit down. I have noticed that those suffering from low mood or depression often knit using subdued colours or blacks, beiges and greys. I encourage those suffering from depression to choose vibrant, soft yarns.

In contrast, those who have a tendency to be a little manic seem to prefer vivid, almost neon colours, so I would advise toning down your choice of colour if this is the case.

Notes

Occasionally people suffering from fibromyalgia and ME are unable to tolerate touching bright colours – the sensory input appears to be too great – but I have discovered they can be introduced in a gradual way, for example by using darker colours flecked with brighter tones to begin with.

Knitting is an activity which many people find they CAN do even when they feel unable to do anything else. The benefit of being successful at something is very powerful.

Many knitters strive to complete a single project before allowing themselves to start another. Most do this to avoid building a massive stash and never completing a task. Whereas I wouldn't advocate continuing to spend on materials for large numbers of projects at one time, my experience is that to gain maximum benefit it's helpful to plan a range of projects to address specific needs and moods.

Switch between these projects as you feel the need and don't set yourself deadlines – certainly not tight ones as these will increase your levels of stress.

Take advantage of knitting's portability to plan a range of projects you can use in a number of situations.

"I often have knitting with me, something small to work on while waiting in lines, or to take with me on my lunch hour."

A simple yet powerful solution

Notes

With the advances in commercial manufacturing and dyeing, beautifully coloured, softly textured yarn doesn't have to be expensive, so shop around. Having said that, there's no doubt that a bit of luxury goes a long way to making us feel great. There are few things better than knitting with luscious yarns in fab colours and textures using beautiful needles that feel good in your hands.

Touch and vision are powerful sensations so take advantage of them to extend your knitting experience. Relish rich colours and how the yarn feels in your hands.

If money is short, there are some great acrylic brands on the market including self-patterning ones, but next time you are asked what you want for your birthday or Christmas, why not ask for some luxury yarn or needles?

There are numerous projects to choose from and always something to learn whatever your skill level.

When planning your projects, bear in mind their nature, and the materials needed.

Plan them with specific aims in mind and swap between them according to your mood of the moment.

POINTS TO PERUSE

1. Take time to plan a range of projects to maximise the benefits and address specific issues. Swap between them according to how you feel and what you'd like to achieve.

2. Use an 'intricate' project to distract your mind from any life problems or symptoms of illness such as pain. It will put you in control.

3. Learn a new skill regularly, so always have a 'novelty' project on the go. It will be good for your brain health. Give yourself time to learn and remember it's about the rhythm of the process.

4. Allow your mind to roam without limit with an 'automatic' easy project. It will give your mind a mini break from the problems of daily life.

Notes

A simple yet powerful solution

5. Enjoy the journey involved in a 'big', longer-term project. It will give you a huge sense of achievement. Don't set yourself a deadline for completion, add to it when you feel the desire.

6. Raise your mood with a 'quick-fix' small project in your favourite colour and soft texture.

7. Keep a 'bag' project handy in your bag for knitting out and about, on the go, in emergencies, on long journeys or your commute to work.

8. Explore your creativity with a pattern-free, 'free knitting' project. It will enable you to nourish and grow your creative ability and help you to let go of mistakes. Go with the flow and take your time to explore.

Notes

My Notes

A simple yet powerful solution

-9-
TAKE
ACTION

Use it,
don't lose it!

· ·

The brilliant thing about knitting is...

it enables you to take action

any time, anywhere...

Notes

Reading this book is your first step on your way to wellness, but becoming engaged in the 'doing' is what makes the real difference – it will enable you to succeed and stay motivated.

You're much more likely to be successful if you are involved in 'doing'. Being actively engaged, as opposed to being a passive recipient, carries much more opportunity for success.

All success needs action and perseverance, so now to the most important part... the doing.

In Therapeutic Knitting the primary focus of your knitting changes away from the end product to the actual process – learning to get your mind into the flow of the movement.

Don't rush towards producing an end product. Let it take time and allow the rhythm of the process to take over.

Focusing on the process rather than the end product doesn't remove the purpose. Having a purpose to your knitting is important, but this doesn't necessarily have to be a specific end product. For some, the purpose may be to achieve a calm mind or a better night's sleep and this may become more important than the actual knitted item. Again, you will find that this changes according to your mood at the time.

On some occasions you will only want to knit for the process, on others you may be keen to see the end product – it will depend on how you feel in the moment.

A simple yet powerful solution

Data from the Stitchlinks / Cardiff University study[1] suggest
that seasoned knitters may already be focusing more on the
actual process rather than the end product. 67% of those who
responded rated the importance of the process at 8–10 on a
scale of 0–10 where 0 was 'not at all' and 10 was 'very'.

*"Knitting is calming, it helps with concentration and calms.
The benefits are like meditation or prayer."*

If you have low self-confidence or have been unwell for some
time, you may feel a bit 'closed down' and a little fearful of
trying new things. You may feel your creative self has shut
down. Knitting will enable you to feel safe within the structure
of your knitted item, but at the same time won't pose any
restrictions on what you can potentially create. Take small
steps, and as your confidence improves, increase those steps.
In this way you can gradually learn to just enjoy 'having a go'
to a point where you are perfectly happy to experiment. Stick
at it and the benefits will come.

Making mistakes, and learning from them, is an important
part of the learning experience. In the Stitchlinks / Cardiff
University study[1], knitters told us knitting has taught them
it is OK to make mistakes – mistakes aren't catastrophic. They
have learned that mistakes can be undone and you can still
reach your end goal despite a few detours along the way.
Often that end goal is richer because of the lessons learned.
Knitters will tell you that they learn more about the structure
of knitting through the mistakes they have made. To pick up

Notes

Notes

the point I made in Chapter 4, it can be beneficial to your wellbeing to learn to let 'mistakes' go and to view them as a way of introducing character and uniqueness to your work.

*　　*　　*

How you get started will depend on whether you are new to knitting or an experienced knitter who would like to use your craft as a therapeutic tool to improve your wellness.

Either way, you can get going even without a pattern. Indeed, when I'm introducing new knitters to Therapeutic Knitting it can be quite some time before they progress to following a written pattern, and some never wish to.

The important initial goal is to get your mind into the flow of the movements and your hands working in harmony with your mind.

For new knitters, I will cast on 25-30 stitches for them and teach the knit stitch using the words, 'in', 'around', 'through' and 'off' to accompany the appropriate movements. Quietly repeating these words not only helps to remember the movements but encourages your mind into a meditative-like state – into the flow of the movements. By beginning this way, newcomers can experience the meditative-like, calming benefits quickly without getting frustrated and tied up in learning to cast on or reading a pattern. You can introduce the purl stitch when the knit stitch has been mastered and the movements are flowing.

A simple yet powerful solution

Working without a pattern in this way enables you to learn new skills and develops creative ability within a safe structure – a square or rectangle for example. Having no pattern to follow means you can experiment with different stitch combinations whenever you feel like it. Even if you're an experienced knitter it's a good idea to have a 'free knitting' project on the go to encourage and enable you to knit with your creative mind – with freedom.

> *"Knitting opens up a secret door,*
> *and lets everything flow freely.*
> *Thoughts, emotions, everything."*

If you normally knit very quickly, try experimenting with slowing your movements down. It will enable you to be more aware of the rhythm of the process, of how the needles feel in your hands and how the texture and colour of the yarn impact on you – this will increase your awareness of the information entering your brain from your hands.

You can see the knitting process in action on YouTube where there are numerous videos available on all aspects of knitting.

If you are prone to aching hands and wrists it may be necessary to pace your knitting. Even if you are fit and well, limiting your time knitting in one session can help to prevent problems later down the line. Those who have hand, arm or neck pain should pay more attention to pacing as this will

Notes

enable you to continue the craft you love. To reiterate the point I made in Chapter 6, sitting for long periods is harmful to your health, so spread your knitting out over the course of the day rather than doing it all in one big chunk. This approach will also mean you'll reap the benefits, such as the feelings of calm and happiness, across the day too.

If you already have hand pain and are new to knitting then it would be sensible to start slowly and build up the amount you do gradually. Start with 25-30 stitches on your needles. If possible, ask someone else to do this for you as it will enable you to concentrate on learning the knit stitch and getting your mind into the flow of the movement. At this point, it's important to realise that this doesn't mean you have to knit all 30 stitches in one go – the beauty of knitting is that you can pick it up and drop it anytime.

I would recommend that you knit as many stitches as you are able until you just feel your hands beginning to ache. Take a note of the number of stitches and make a point of knitting two stitches fewer next time – at this stage the aim is to stop just before you feel pain or trigger an increase in any pain which may normally be present.

Another brilliant thing about knitting is that it gives you wonderful visual feedback – every stitch you do is a step towards the end of the row or the end of the project. For now, your focus should be on getting your mind into the flow of the movements.

A simple yet powerful solution

Once you've established your baseline number of stitches and your hands are comfortable with this level of activity, you can begin to gradually build up the number of stitches you knit at any one time. This approach will improve the strength and stamina of your hand muscles and the mobility of the joints without causing any discomfort.

Don't worry if you're not able to knit many stitches at first. It's quite common for patients I see to only be able to knit five to ten stitches before they need a break to rest and stretch their hands. If this is the case, I would recommend you knit little and often – depending on how much exercise your hands can tolerate over the course of a day. Some of my patients like to knit for five or ten minutes every hour or a few times a day depending on their individual circumstances and needs. You will need to find your own individual baseline.

The principle of pacing is used widely on pain management programmes, but it is a useful technique to be aware of even if you're fit and well. It's all about not overdoing activities to a point which renders you unable to function on subsequent days. Even the fittest of us has done this at some point. It's about planning and keeping your activities at a level which enables you to perform well every day – keeping things on an even keel rather than following a boom / bust path.

Those of you who are currently unwell may already have discovered that doing too much of any activity too fast

Notes

Notes

results in exhaustion and potentially pain. In pain management terms this is called the overactivity / underactivity cycle, and these are easy to fall into even if you're well because we all have good and bad days.

This cycle describes the person trying to fit in as much as possible on 'good' days, then 'paying the price' on subsequent days. Life becomes a series of very full 'doing' days followed by a few 'not able to do anything' days. If you recognise this pattern, then pacing is the way to go. Even if you don't have this problem, being sensible about not knitting for long periods without a break can prevent repetitive strain injury (RSI) in the future.

A good pacing regime aims at enabling you to 'do' every day – it enables you to even out activity levels by breaking up projects into manageable chunks. So you knit for a bit, stopping just **BEFORE** you feel pain (with a bit of trial and error you'll learn where this level is), then move on to either rest or to do another activity involving a completely different hand movement such as card making or scrapbooking, perhaps. You can go back to your knitting later in the day or do a little every hour depending on how your hands feel.

Pacing doesn't mean staying at the same level or not making progress. On the contrary, it enables you to move forward in a controlled way. You should still strive to improve and learn new skills. Pacing is about not overdoing activities but still pushing yourself to your comfortable limit in whatever

A simple yet powerful solution

activities you do in life. When you feel the time is right to move on and do more, then it's important to keep improving.

The trick is to find the level at which you are able to perform without increasing symptoms but then gradually pushing at this limit to encourage progression and improvement. It may seem a little frustrating at first, particularly when you're engrossed in your project, but it should enable you to knit regularly and reach your goal in a similar length of time without increasing any discomfort if you're prone to achy hands. It will feel even more frustrating to be forced to take a few days off because you've overdone it.

Once you have mastered the knit stitch and feel you are 'in the flow', take some time to reflect on the sensation. You may have forgotten what it feels like to be truly relaxed. Enjoy the sensation and learn what it feels like then practise recalling the feeling at times when you don't have your knitting to hand. It will help you to make regular relaxation a habit in your life.

> *"It wasn't until I started knitting every day*
> *that I really felt at peace."*

You can enhance this recall process by visualising the process of knitting. The technique requires you to visualise yourself actually doing the movement to be effective. So you 'feel' your hands moving in the same way (although they remain

Notes

still) whilst imagining the needles and the texture of the yarn moving through your fingers – it's not simply a question of watching yourself knitting in your mind, there's a subtle difference. It takes a little practise but will reap rewards when mastered and I talk more about this in Chapter 10.

Visualising or imagining movement fires off the same neural pathways as actually performing the movement, it just stops short of actually activating the necessary muscles. Visualisation is a skill used by athletes enabling them to improve their performance and perfect their technique even when they are injured.

As with everything in life it's important to make progress, to move on, otherwise life can feel a bit stagnant, a little boring. We all need to keep learning and exploring new paths to maintain interest, wellbeing and brain health.

Science has shown us that it's important to keep learning throughout life – it encourages new brain cells to form and new neural pathways to open even in old age. Novelty is good for you. Importantly we know that brain cells die if you sit unoccupied. As with muscles it's a case of 'use it, or lose it'. So make a point not to get stuck in a rut with your knitting or lifestyle in general.

Do something different or learn something new on a regular basis, don't wait for things to begin feeling stale.

A simple yet powerful solution

Make a start at 'the doing' today, however small a step, and then keep at it.

Learn to get your mind into the flow of the movement. Stick at it and the benefits will flow too.

By taking action you've already begun the life-changing process that will enable you to take control and move forward.

Use it, don't lose it today.

Notes

POINTS TO PERUSE

1. Focus on the feeling of deep relaxation and learn what it feels like. Practise recalling this feeling at times when you don't have your knitting to hand.

2. Ask someone else to cast on 25-30 stitches for you if you are completely new to knitting. Begin by concentrating on learning the knit stitch.

3. Quietly repeat the words 'in', 'around', 'through' and 'off' as you learn the knit stitch. It will help to get your mind into the flow of the movements.

4. Have a purpose to your knitting. This doesn't have to be producing an end product. It can be to relax, experience calm, manage stress or improve your sleep, for example.

Notes

A simple yet powerful solution

5. Enjoy the safety of knitting if your self-confidence is low. However, learn to push your limits to develop and explore your creativity from this secure foundation.

6. Have a go. View 'mistakes' as a way to learn and a way of introducing character and uniqueness into your work. Enjoy being happy to experiment.

7. Pace your knitting to prevent hand problems. It will enable you to continue to enjoy your craft for a long time. Find your baseline activity and build your strength and stamina from there.

8. Spread your knitting activity over the day. If you are working, knit a little during your lunch break and on your commute. It will enable you will reap the benefits throughout the day.

Notes

My Notes

A simple yet powerful solution

-10-
WHOLE-PERSON HEALTH CARE

Take charge of your health and wellness

· ·

The brilliant thing about knitting is...
it offers an accessible means of living
well despite health problems...

Notes

This book is about using knitting to improve your wellbeing whether you are fit and well or living with a long-term medical condition. This chapter focuses on taking Therapeutic Knitting a step further by looking at how you can use knitting to complement medical treatment to enable a whole-person approach to your health care.

Knitters already use their craft to manage a range of medical conditions. To date, over 60 different conditions have been mentioned in the stories I've received. Most of these have depression, stress, persistent pain, sleep disturbance and social isolation at their core – issues that affect millions of people across the globe.

Life is a mixture of good and bad experiences. When you suffer ill health you tend to have fewer positive experiences, so it is beneficial to actively focus on increasing these. This book was written to enable you to do just that.

"Knitting calms me down when I'm stressed,
gets me excited when it feels like there's no point living,
gives me something to think about that is outside myself,
a reason to get up in the morning."

When you live with a long-term illness it can be overwhelming. Your 'creative self' may have shut down as you struggle to survive life's stresses, low mood or pain. Surviving the added demands and complications of living with ill health can take up all available energy, so as Maslow suggested, there is little

A simple yet powerful solution

time left to deal with the higher functioning needs which enable you to reach your full potential. If you feel this way then it will help to prioritise a daily session of knitting to deliberately nurture your creative passion.

If you are some years down the road of living with a long-term medical condition, or if life events have eroded your self-esteem and confidence, you may, understandably, be wary of trying something new. This can make developing creativity and learning new skills more of a challenge. Knitting, however, will enable you to develop creative thought within a safe framework. It will help you to feel safe as you explore and experiment.

Creativity and structure may seem strange bedfellows, but the structure is needed in order to nurture creative thought and ability from a point where it may have become completely closed down or seem inaccessible because of life events. Knitting will enable you to move from a point where there is safety in structure through to a point where you are happy to experiment with a range of open-ended options.

> *"Through harnessing your own creativity you can reconnect not only with yourself but with others, therefore strengthening community via conversation."*

When knitters encounter a problem with their knitting, they seek to find a solution. This often involves trial and error or asking other knitters either via online or face-to-face groups,

Notes

email or YouTube. Developing an attitude of seeking to solve problems and learning that problems are surmountable by thinking creatively will help you to manage life's challenges in new ways.

The creative process will take you outside yourself and any personal challenges, enabling you to view problems with a different perspective.

Explorers and experimenters view not reaching their desired outcome as a means of learning about what works and what doesn't, so have at least one project on the go where you become a knitting explorer. It will help you on the path to becoming a life explorer. Being a life explorer is fun.

*   *   *

We all suffer from low mood from time to time, but as many as one in three people will suffer from clinical depression at some stage in their lives.

In our Stitchlinks / Cardiff University study[1] 81% of those with clinical depression who responded said they usually or definitely felt happier after knitting.

54% of those with depression reported feeling happy or very happy after knitting. Less than 1% remained sad.

"Antidepressants numb all my senses.
Knitting makes me happy."

A simple yet powerful solution

Those suffering from depression particularly benefited from belonging to a knitting group.

Performed regularly, knitting can enhance positively-focused thought patterns and pathways.

> *"I have recently begun knitting and have completed several projects and have had a wonderful change in my mental attitude since finding the benefits of this craft."*

Knitters tell of how knitting helps them organise their thoughts and of thoughts becoming more positive. Some use knitting to help them think through dark thoughts without becoming stressed by them. This enables them to identify options and potential solutions, or to file away unpleasant memories. Some use this technique to enable them to reflect on, and process, 'therapy' sessions.

If you have a tendency to think negatively you can use your knitting to plan forwards and think about positive events. The more you do this, the more thinking positively will become a habit – it's about developing positive, constructive habits of thinking and behaviour. Remember, the way you feel is directly connected to how you think, and with a little perseverance it is possible to change your thinking habits.

Your thoughts, behaviour and feelings are inextricably knitted together.

Notes

Having projects and group meetings to look forward to will encourage you to look forward to tomorrow. Some stories have told of how this can prevent suicide.

> *"I firmly believe that having my knitting to get*
> *out of bed for and take my mind off things*
> *saved my life – I cannot imagine surviving*
> *how bad I felt otherwise."*

> *"If I hadn't kept myself occupied with knitting,*
> *I would have hibernated to the point of death.*
> *It gave me something else to think about,*
> *and at the end of the day I had something*
> *to show for the effort of staying alive."*

You have the power to retrain and reshape your mind and Therapeutic Knitting can help.

> *"I look forward to waking up, I can imagine how*
> *my projects will turn out and be excited by the prospect.*
> *My life has changed beyond recognition."*

Perfectionists often have health issues. Setting impossible goals and having difficulty accepting that nothing in the real world is ever perfect creates a state of constant ongoing stress, worry and muscle tension. These can become major factors and cause damaging health consequences. A period of daily 'quiet knitting' will help you to manage your stress

A simple yet powerful solution

levels and any symptoms. You can also use your knitting to help you modify your perfectionist tendencies to prevent future problems arising, as I discussed in Chapter 4.

If anxiety and panic are issues for you, carry a 'bag' project. When you feel the first symptoms arising, immerse yourself in your knitting, taking your mind into the flow of the rhythmic movements. Many knitters are managing anxiety and panic successfully in this way and tell me that simply the knowledge they have an effective tool at hand is often enough to ward off symptoms – it will give you confidence to go out, to socialise and to travel on public transport.

Knitting, or visualisation of knitting, can help in most situations you may be fearful of. People who suffer from panic attacks and agoraphobia use visualisation successfully. Visualisation, and recalling the feeling of knitting, can be useful whilst sitting in the dentist's chair and before exams, public speaking or interviews. There is great potential for knitting and visualising to be used as a tool to enable you to socialise or deal with situations you may otherwise find threatening.

Why not practise visualising knitting on a regular basis to perfect the technique? It will help you to keep calm next time you need a helping hand, particularly when the situation may not be conducive to knitting – you'll have an immediately accessible solution in mind. It is about building new, positive habits – the more you keep at it and practise, the better.

Notes

Notes

If anxiety causes you problems with air flight, some airlines will allow wooden circular needles. If this isn't possible, visualising the movements will help you achieve a level of calm, so why not get your visualisation skills down to a fine art in preparation for your next plane flight?

A portable project will also help if you suffer from persistent pain. One in five people do, and there are many ways knitting can help. The experience of pain is heavily dependent on the context within which your brain interprets incoming danger signals. Low mood, loneliness, lack of occupation, lack of success, having nothing to look forward to, worry, fear and stress all play a part in increasing the experience of pain. The activity itself can also distract your brain's attention, as can planning future projects and thinking creatively. Managed distraction can give you back control and significantly change your outlook on life. Think back to those Core Issues in Chapter 1 and take steps to ameliorate these states by actively using your knitting as a tool.

"Knitting means I can subjugate pain to the status of discomfort. The movement needed by knitting seems to create a state of mind in which I'm more able to downgrade pain to a background feature."

Pain clinics around the world are following my lead and including Therapeutic Knitting groups in services they offer.

A simple yet powerful solution

*"I can focus on the repetition instead of the pain.
I can make things for those in need instead
of laying around being a person in need. Now that
I am coming to the end of my surgeries,
I find that others are asking me to teach them
knitting or crochet. Now, instead of just helping
me de-stress and ignore pain, it is moving into
a reason for socialisation and bringing joy to others."*

The technique of focusing forward on to future or special projects can also be helpful if you are awaiting a hospital admission or a procedure which might involve pain. It is known that if you anticipate pain, the experience will be more intense when it arrives. By choosing a special knitting project with luxurious yarn to look forward to, and focusing on this project, you can divert your brain's attention onto more positive events. The trick is to tell yourself that you can't start your special project until you are actually in hospital and then look forward to knitting it – it takes the focus of attention off the unknown onto a positive activity with a known feel-good experience.

Pain researcher David Butler talks about having your own 'personal drugs cabinet in your brain' which is full of 'happy hormones'[25,26]. This 'cabinet' which contains your own, natural pain killers can be opened by positive mood, knowledge about your condition, goals, support, laughter and the need to survive. It is closed by worry, fear, stress, loneliness and poor coping. The power of your own 'drugs cabinet' is immense.

Notes

Getting enough good quality sleep is a big problem for many. You may find it difficult to 'switch off' or you may wake in the early hours and find your thoughts, and angry feelings at not being able to sleep, keep you awake.

Knitting for twenty minutes or so before sleep will help you 'switch off' those incessant thought processes to aid a peaceful sleep.

If you have a tendency to wake in the early hours, keep a knitting kit by your bedside and use it to calm stressful thoughts or manage pain. I would advise a bit of 'free knitting' so your brain doesn't become over stimulated by reading a pattern. Use wooden needles if sleeping with a partner as clicking metal ones might not go down well. Knitters report a significant decrease in the frequency of nightmares too.

Those with symptoms of post traumatic stress also report significant improvement in the frequency of flashbacks. This may be explained by the study carried out at Oxford University into visuo-spatial movement I mentioned in Chapter 2[9,10].

I talked about the need to manage stress on a daily basis in Chapter 4. When it gets out of control it can cause actual physical and mental health symptoms. The symptoms, in turn, will cause more stress. High levels of stress also affect your immune system which will increase your chances of getting a disease which will make you ill.

A simple yet powerful solution

Returning to the point I made in Chapter 7, it is common to find your stress levels reflected in the tension of your stitches. Personal tension translates into increased knitting tension. Use this to your advantage by deliberately relaxing your stitches to ease tension levels all around.

If your stress levels are high it's even more important to take time out every day with some 'quiet' knitting to actively lower them. Combining this with enjoying the company of friends in a supportive group gives you a powerful tool to keep harmful levels of stress at bay.

*   *   *

The reward system in the brain fires off when you are successful at a task which requires a little effort and results in a flush of feel-good and pain relieving chemicals. You can take advantage of this to raise your mood and manage pain.

This circuit is also active in addictive behaviour. The resultant chemical release makes it difficult to break addictive habits because it makes you feel good, so in order to maintain the feeling you need to maintain the habit.

The possible involvement of the reward system in knitting may explain why knitters report successfully using their craft to conquer addictive habits – knitting may be replacing a destructive habit with a constructive activity. Knitting keeps the hands and mind busy but also fills the time void left when an addiction is stopped, as well as providing alternative

Notes

safe social contact. Having too much time, isolation and chemical cravings are the reasons why addicts often fail.

"I discovered that having my hands occupied was soothing and meant I could avoid smoking, drinking or eating through boredom and distress."

Knitters use knitting to break a range of addictions and bad habits, ranging from heroin and alcohol to smoking, binge eating, snacking and even hair and eyebrow pulling. If you have a habit you'd like to kick – perhaps it's evening snacking – consider using knitting to support you through.

"Ever since I quit smoking two and a half years ago, I almost always have knitting with me wherever I go. The difference is that where my cigarettes were an anxiety crutch, my knitting allows for a positive outcome."

It is also easy to become heavily reliant on medication. Medication is effective when it is used appropriately with a specific purpose. When monitored carefully, it can enable you to be proactive in your care, but it shouldn't be the central or only focus of your wellness action plan.

Remember, the factors that influence how you feel are so much greater than the issues which can be addressed with medication alone.

A simple yet powerful solution

Notes

Many wish to cut down their medication to reduce unwanted side effects and successfully use their knitting to enable them to do this. Getting absorbed in the flow of an activity can alter your perception of time and you can make use of this, and knitting's distractive qualities, to gradually reduce amounts being taken. However, **you should always do this under medical supervision.**

Breaking any habit needs to be taken step-by-step, focusing on being successful in the moment. Being successful in that small step will boost your confidence and will move you forward – **taking action and moving forward feels good.** This will keep you motivated and help you to persevere on your quest to quit your habit.

> *"Knitting allows me some measure of control when it comes to my medications and allows me to be an active participant in managing my pain, and from there my health."*

Therapeutic Knitting can also be beneficial for those suffering bereavement. In the period between the death and the funeral it can be difficult to function at all. Knitting will calm your mind to help you survive the high stress and sleep problems during this challenging time.

Therapeutic Knitting enables you to listen to your body and take the time out you need to begin the healing process.

Notes

Knitting together with friends can be highly beneficial at this stage – it can enable you to be in the comforting presence of supportive friends without feeling the need to contribute or talk. It gives your bodymind space to heal.

* * *

We all have days when we feel downright blaaaah, and if you're suffering from a long-term illness, flare-up days are inevitable. Learning to accept these as part of life's normal ups and downs will take away some of the frustration. Your knitting can help you in this process.

You can make these days much more bearable if you plan for them in advance. Have some pre-cooked, 'flare-up freezer meals' handy and a supply of good knitting books and magazines put aside for such an event. Put your feet up, listen to relaxing music and spend some enjoyable time planning your future projects. This process will keep your mind focused on positive, forward thinking issues rather than dwelling on more negative events which could otherwise be the case when you're having a bad day, whatever the reason. This will help to prevent you falling back into those destructive, negative thinking loops.

In the Stitchlinks / Cardiff University study[1], 72% of those who responded reported knitting more than three times a week, and we found a significant relationship between frequency of knitting and perceived happiness, calm, confidence, concentration, problem-solving abilities and thinking. They describe knitting as *"bringing creativity into daily life"*. This enables them to feel more adventurous and prepared to try new things and learn new skills.

Your mind, like your muscles, grows stronger and more efficient with good use.

Therapeutic Knitting can be taken a step further to complement medical treatment to enable a whole-person approach to your health care.

You CAN make progress on this pathway today and you CAN be successful. You CAN thrive.

Therapeutic Knitting can improve your health and wellness, whether you are fit and healthy or unwell.

Being proactive in taking responsibility for your own health, whether it is in a preventative way or in dealing with ill health, will maximise your healing potential.

Use your knitting together with the information in this book to take charge of your health and wellbeing today.

Enjoy each moment on your way to wellness.

Notes

POINTS TO PERUSE

1. Join a knitting group if you suffer from depression. It will increase the benefits and enable you to meet and make supportive friends within the safety of the group.

2. Practise visualising knitting, particularly if you suffer from anxiety and panic. It will help you to stay calm even when you don't have your knitting readily available.

3. Knit before bed for a more restful sleep and keep a project by your bed for those nights when you wake in the early hours. It will keep you calm and relaxed.

4. Treat yourself to a special project if you're scheduled to go into hospital or have a painful procedure. Look forward to starting it to focus your mind on a positive, constructive activity.

Notes

5. Knit to ease persistent pain – it can work to improve your life on many levels. A 'bag' kit will help you manage symptoms whilst out and about.

6. Use the tension of your knitting as feedback for how stressed you are and deliberately seek to knit with looser stitches whilst relaxing into the movements.

7. Break addictive habits with the help of your knitting. It can enable you to stop smoking, lose weight and even help with drug and alcohol problems.

8. Become a knitting explorer. Learn to be happy experimenting. It will help you to become a life explorer and open up a world of opportunities.

Notes

My Notes

A simple yet powerful solution

EPILOGUE

Open doors and jump
on your springboard to life

• •

The brilliant thing about knitting is...

it ignites a desire

to live life well...

Notes

This book is about using knitting as a tool to improve your health and wellness to enable you to live a more fulfilled life.

It is about using knitting to nurture a creative, flexible mind to enable you to deal with life's inevitable challenges and live well despite them.

It isn't about encouraging you to sit and knit all day. On the contrary, it is about inspiring you to learn a wide-range of skills, to explore the opportunities life has to offer, to enable you to experience more positive moments in life, whether you are fit and healthy or suffering ill health.

The Core Issues identified in Chapter 1 play a large part in how we all manage life, health and wellness. Therapeutic Knitting can help you deal with these issues and ride with the flow of inevitable change.

If you are unwell, Therapeutic Knitting can complement any medical treatment as part of a whole-person approach to your health and wellness. Linked to healthcare environments, Therapeutic Knitting groups can help to address your illness within the context of your bigger picture.

It is about taking a whole-person approach to wellbeing, being well and healing.

Learning to knit can open a door to the world and enable you to enjoy its numerous exciting opportunities.

A simple yet powerful solution

This book shows you how the activity of knitting gets you involved in 'doing'. The knowledge and action combined, will give you a powerful tool at hand any time, anywhere.

Remember, success needs action and perseverance so keep at it and the benefits will come.

Make a decision now to take action, and this moment will signify the start of your new life. Look forward, have fun and enjoy.

Support is there for you to do this through the Stitchlinks website and forum where you can share your experiences with friends who understand and care, so you are not on your own.

Open that door to opportunity.

The brilliant thing about knitting is you can start today from your armchair.

It's your simple yet powerful way to wellness and it is in your hands.

"Knitting heals from within."

Notes

"I am convinced that the repetitive meditative and creative aspects of knitting are what has gently helped me back into a more fulfilling life.

"I have absolutely no doubt that knitting daily for over six months 'reset' my brain in some way, and also that Stitchlinks allowed me to open up again after the long years of dealing with illness and disability on my own had just worn me down and closed me down.

"Thank you so very much for what you are doing."

A simple yet powerful solution

A KNITTER'S STORY

"My doctor diagnosed depression in January this year and put me on anti-depressants. I also found a counsellor to talk through some issues with me but I needed something that was truly mine.

"I'd been doing a lot of abstract cross stitch work, but I no longer had the concentration for it and my eyes were tired after working at a computer all day – knitting was the obvious choice.

"I started with simple patterns that required little thought, then I started to get more complicated. I joined online forums (at last, I had people I could talk to about something that interested me), then I started to take projects into work with me to do at breaks and lunchtimes – what a great conversation starter. I've discovered so many fellow knitters and crafters.

"I go looking for yarn and needles wherever I go and take mum along with me – shopping has a new dimension as I examine knitted items in stores to work out how to make them myself (and sell if I can as a second source of income) – now I have something that is mine, creative, and possibly income generating. A source of conversation, passion and interest to share with my mum (who shares this with friends) and with people everywhere.

"Getting my needles and wool out in public is now second nature – I take it wherever I go – and it forces me to enjoy the cup of coffee rather than just bolt it down and rush on to the next thing – I need to finish the row, the pattern repeat, another few stitches – and suddenly half an hour has passed.

"Knitting at home prevents me picking at chocolate and biscuits or booze (you can't knit drunk!) and I'm not seeing my counsellor any more, and I'm off the drugs.

"Each week I have a new project to look forward to, and each week I finish a project; I'm getting commissions for colleagues and strangers – particularly for baby clothes – small and quick projects – and I now get a sense of satisfaction for a job well done – something that was lacking in my life. I still don't get paid enough at work, I still don't use all my talents at work, I still don't get total job satisfaction at work, but I do get all those things at home when knitting. The work life balance is getting better.

"The rhythmic nature of knitting slows me down – the continuous counting of stitches or rows for some patterns calms my mind and stops that 'worrying' about work and other issues; the sense of satisfaction as you complete a project – money just can't buy that.

"Knitting as therapy – of course. I wouldn't question it for a moment – it has given me part of my life back."

A simple yet powerful solution

REFERENCES

1. Riley, J., Corkhill, B. & Morris, C. (2013). The Benefits of Knitting for Personal and Social Wellbeing in Adulthood: Findings from an International Survey. *British Journal of Occupational Therapy,* 76(2), 50-57.

2. Lambert, K. G. (2006). Rising rates of depression in today's society: Consideration of the roles of effort-based rewards and enhanced resilience in day-to-day functioning. *Neuroscience and Biobehavioral Reviews,* 30, 497-510.

3. Lambert, K. G. (2008). *Lifting Depression: A neuroscientist's hands-on approach to activating your brain's healing power.* New York: Basic Books.

4. Gallace, A., Torta, D. M. E., Moseley, G. L. & Iannetti, G. D. (2011). The analgesic effect of crossing the arms. *Pain,* 152, 1418-1423.

5. Jacobs, B. & Fornal, C. A. (1999). Activity of Serotonergic Neurons in Behaving Animals. *Neuropsychopharmacology,* 21, 9s-15s.

6. Jacobs, B., Fornal, C. & Martin-Cora, F. (2002). Activity of Medullary Serotonergic Neurons in Freely Moving Animals. *Brain Research Reviews,* 40, 45-52.

7. Davidson, R. J., Kabat-Zinn, J., Schumacher, J., Rosenkranz, M., Muller, D., Santorelli, S. F., Urbanowski, F., Harrington, A., Bonus, K. & Sheridan, J. F. (2003). Alterations in brain and immune function produced by mindfulness meditation. *Psychosomatic Medicine,* 65, 564-570.

8. Kabat-Zinn, J. (1996). *Full Catastrophe Living. How to cope with stress pain and illness using mindfulness meditation.* Revised edition. Piatkus.

9. Holmes, E. A., Brewin, C. R. & Hennessy, R. G. (2004). Trauma films, information processing, and intrusive memory development. *Journal of Experimental Psychology*: General, 133(1), 3-22. doi: 10.1037/0096-3445.133.1.3

10. Holmes, E. A., James, E. L., Coode-Bate, T. & Deeprose, C. (2009). Can Playing the Computer Game 'Tetris' Reduce the Build-up of Flashbacks for Trauma?' A Proposal from Cognitive Science. *PLoS ONE*, 4(1), e4153. doi: 10.1371 / journal. pone.0004153.

11. Wilson, F. (1999). *The Hand; How it shapes the brain, language and human culture.* New York: Vintage Books.

12. Moll, J., Krueger, F., Zahn, R., Pardini, M., de Oliveira-Suza, R. & Grafman, J. (2006). Human fronto-mesolimbic networks guide decisions about charitable donation. Proceedings of the National Academy of Sciences, 103(42),15623-15628.

13. Gerard Allt. I Knit London. Shop and sanctuary for knitters. 106 Lower Marsh, London SE1 7AB.

14. Hawkley, L. C., Cacioppo, J. T. (2010) Loneliness Matters: A Theoretical and Empirical View of Consequences and Mechanisms. *Annals of Behavioral Medicine*, 40, 218-227.

15. Valenzuela, M. J., Matthews, F. E., Brayne, C., Ince, P., Halliday, G., Kril, J. J., Dalton, M. A., Richardson, K., Forster, G. & Sachdev, P. (2012). Multiple Biological Pathways Link Cognitive Lifestyle to Protection from Dementia. *Biological Psychiatry*, 71(9), 783-791.

16. Hinzey, A. & DeVries, C. (2012). Social contact can ease pain related to nerve damage. Poster No. 786.04. Neuroscience 2012, New Orleans, USA.

17. Campaign to End Loneliness, Age UK Oxfordshire. (2012). *Loneliness – the state we're in*. Retrieved 13th March 2014 from *www.campaigntoendloneliness.com*.

18. Butler, D. S. & Moseley, G. L. (2003) *Explain Pain*. Australia: Noigroup Publications.

19. Dunbar, R. I. M., Baron, R., Frangou, A., Pearce, E., van Leeuwin, E. J. C., Stow, J., Partridge, G., MacDonald, I., Barra, V. & van Vugt, M. (2011) Social laughter is correlated with an elevated pain threshold. Proceedings of the Royal Society for Biological Sciences, 1373.

20. Wilmot, E. G., Edwardson, C. L., Achana, F. A., Davies, M. J., Gorely, T., Gray, L. J., Khunti, K., Yates, T. & Biddle, S. J. H. (2012). Sedentary time in adults and the association with diabetes, cardiovascular disease and death: systematic review and meta-analysis. *Diabetologia*, 55, 2895-2905.

21. Harlow, H. F. (1959). Love in Infant Monkeys. *Scientific American* 200, no. 6, 68-74.

22. Watson, N. M., Wells, T. J. & Cox, C. (1998). Rocking chair therapy for dementia patients: its effect on psychosocial well-being and balance. *American Journal of Alzheimer's Disease and Other Dementias*, 13(6), 296-308.

23. Xu, T., Yu, X., Perlik, A. J., Tobin, W. F., Zweig, J. A., Tennant, K., Jones, T. & Zuo, Y. (2009). Rapid formation and selective stabilization of synapses for enduring motor memories. *Nature* 462, 915-919.

24. Greenwood, P. M. & Parasuraman, R. (2010) Neuronal and cognitive plasticity: a neurocognitive framework for ameliorating cognitive aging. Frontiers in Aging Neuroscience. Retrieved March 14th, 2014 from *http://journal.frontiersin.org/ Journal/10.3389fnagi.2010.00150/full.*

25. Butler, D. S., Moseley, G. L., Beames, T. B. & Giles, T. (2012). *The Graded Motor Imagery Handbook*. Australia. Noigroup Publications.

26. Video retrieved April 16th, 2014 from *http://www.youtube. comwatch?v=Gd2NaGZa7M4&feature=youtu.be.*

My Notes

A simple yet powerful solution

Printed in Great Britain
by Amazon